Digital logic gates
and flip-flops

Digital logic gates and flip-flops

What they do and how to use them

Ian R Sinclair

PC Publishing

PC Publishing
4 Brook Street
Tonbridge
Kent TN9 2PJ

First published 1989, reprinted 1990

© PC Publishing

ISBN 1 870775 06 6

British Library Cataloguing in Publication Data

Sinclair, Ian R.
  Digital logic gates and flip-flops.
  1. Digital circuits
  I. Title
  621.38′5′3

  ISBN 1–870775–06–6

Phototypesetting by Scribe Design
Printed and bound by BPCC Wheatons Ltd, Exeter

Preface

Digital logic actions are invariably carried out by integrated circuits, so that the user of the ICs seldom knows what circuits are contained within the chips. This makes it all the more important to be clear about what the ICs do, and that's the subject of this book. The aim is to introduce digital logic, as applied to gates and flip-flops, and show how these circuits carry out their actions. At higher levels, the study of digital logic can be a very mathematical topic, and this book aims to use only the essential mathematics, showing clearly what needs to be known and how it can be applied easily.

A clear understanding of digital logic is as important in servicing as in design and construction, so that the topics that are covered here apply to trouble-shooting as well. By concentrating on gates and flip-flops, which are the elementary digital circuits, the beginner will learn enough digital logic to cope with other types of circuits.

The internals have not been entirely forgotten, and items such as wired-OR and race hazards are clearly explained. The merits and drawbacks of different types of logic chips are noted, but with only passing reference to standard TTL which is little used nowadays. The types of construction that are emphasised are Schottky TTL and high-speed CMOS. Applications of digital logic in computing components such as microprocessors and memory chips are also covered.

The intended readership is the keen amateur, the student, particularly C&G or BTEC, the engineer who knows linear devices well but who has never tackled digital devices, or the technician working in servicing or in design who needs to know more about digital logic circuitry and its applications.

Ian Sinclair

Contents

1 Digital signals

A digital signal is one in which only a few levels of voltage are important, and this number of levels is nearly always two. If you compare a square wave to a sinewave (Figure 1.1), you can see that each part of any one cycle of the sinewave is at a different voltage level; there are as many voltage levels as there are points along the wave that you can sample. By contrast, the square wave has only two important voltage levels, and for most of the time the voltage is steady at one of these levels. When the voltage changes (a voltage transition), it does so as rapidly as possible, and the change

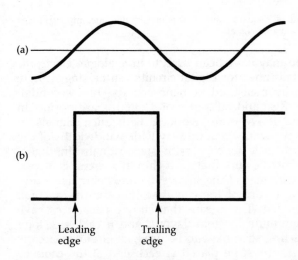

Figure 1.1 Comparing a sinewave (a) with a square wave (b). Only two voltage levels of the square wave are important

1

is always from one of the two possible values to the other. Unlike analogue signals, for which amplitude, frequency and waveform are important measurements, digital signals are of fixed amplitude, so that we are never greatly concerned about amplification, the frequency need not be regular, and the waveform is always the same, a rapid change between two levels.

For a signal like this, the important parts are the changes, the rise and the fall of voltage. The rise time is the time needed for the voltage to change between the 10% and 90% levels (Figure 1.2) and the fall time is the time needed for the voltage to fall from the 90% to the 10% level. Compared with the times (usually times for

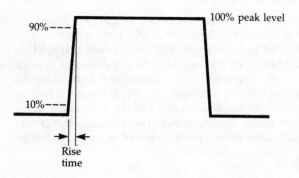

Figure 1.2 The rise time of a square wave. This is usually the most important part of the specification of a digital signal

one cycle) that you may have been used to in analogue electronic circuits, rise and fall times for digital circuits can be staggeringly fast, and are usually measured in nanoseconds (10^{-9} seconds), abbreviated to ns. Rise and fall times of 3 to 50 ns are normal in digital circuits and if we were working with such signals in analogue circuitry we would require very wide bandwidths of the order of 5 MHz upwards to cope with such signals. In digital circuits, we need only be sure that each chip in a circuit can cope with the rise and fall times of the signals that are being used, and design the physical layout of the circuit so that the rise and fall times are not degraded. This means that stray capacitances have to be kept to a minimum by good layout, and if cables or long stretches of connecting strip have to be used, then buffer circuits (such as bus drivers) must be placed at each end of the cable or strip. For most purposes, the rise time is more important than the fall time.

In addition to the care that is needed over signal lines, the power supply lines also need attention. The very short rise and fall times of the signals in digital circuits will inevitably cause pulses to appear on the power supply lines, and these pulses will affect the inputs of other digital circuits. Power supplies must therefore be stabilised, and a decoupling capacitor (usually $0.1\,\mu F$) must be connected between each supply line and earth at each IC. This requirement can be relaxed in some circuits so that only one decoupling capacitor for five or more ICs is used, but in general a high standard of decoupling is needed to maintain a clean supply line voltage.

Signal level

A digital circuit requires an input which is a signal at either one of the two logic input levels, but there has to be a considerable tolerance in each level. The almost universal deployment of +5V power supplies has led to the widespread use of 0V as one level and +5V as the other, but the +5V level really means anything from +3.5V upwards (to the maximum input voltage that the device can handle, which might be around +5.25V), and the 0V level means anything less then about 0.75V.

This tolerance is needed because digital circuits do not amplify signals. The output from a digital circuit is, in fact, often of lower amplitude than the input, so that the +5V level is very seldom achieved at the output, though the 0V level is easier to obtain. At the same time, the tolerance of signal voltage increases the risk of a noise signal being accepted because the voltage difference between the levels is smaller. If the voltage levels were genuinely 0V and +5V, then a noise signal of 5V peak would be needed to provide a false input. If the limits of tolerance are +0.75V and +3.5V, then a noise peak of 2.75V will be enough to cause trouble.

This does not imply that a voltage input of, say 2.0V, will cause any kind of intermediate output. With such an input, the output of a digital circuit will be one level or the other, but you cannot be sure which level. The point of specifying voltages such as +0.7 and +3.5 is that these are guaranteed levels. In a chip that uses these levels, any voltage from +3.5 to +5.25 is guaranteed to be accepted as a high input, and any voltage from +.75V to 0V is guaranteed to be accepted as a low level. A voltage that falls outside these levels will still be taken as either high or low, but the actual result cannot be guaranteed because of manufacturing tolerances. It is almost certain, for example, that a voltage of +1.0V would be taken as low and a voltage of +3.0V as high, but the manufacturers of ICs cannot guarantee this, and it would be a very poor piece of design that relied on the chips to accept these voltage levels.

In addition to the care that is needed over rise and (to a lesser extent) fall times, then, care is needed over signal levels. There is a widespread belief that the voltages of digital signals are unimportant, and this is true in the sense that the precise voltage is of no importance. The maintenance of correct voltage levels is very important, however, and it is easy to forget that a circuit path that involves a set of diodes can bring a 'high' voltage level to below its tolerance value. Three silicon diodes in series, for example, will cause a voltage drop of 1.8V, and with a +5V supply will reduce the high voltage at their output to +3.2V, below the guaranteed 1 level. Circuits like this can work, but they cannot work reliably nor consistently. The whole point of using digital methods is that such circuits when correctly designed will provide standards of reliability and consistency that are unapproachable by any other devices.

The advantage of using ICs exclusively in digital circuits is that the output voltage levels of any IC will be guaranteed to be within the tolerance levels for the input to another IC. Unless the output of an IC is very heavily loaded by being connected with too many other inputs (see fan-out, later), then the use of ICs connected to each other will avoid any problems of signal level. The use of diodes in a signal circuit is always likely to cause problems of signal level and should be avoided. It would be very unusual nowadays to find any circuit applications that required diodes or any potential-dividing circuits to be connected between ICs, so that there should never be any problems about tolerances within a digital circuit in which one device is connected to another of the same 'family'.

Problems can arise, however, at the input to a digital IC. Input signals might come from transducers, switches, or various types of analogue-to-digital converters (AD circuits). The AD circuits will, in general, be ICs which will deliver the correct level of digital signals, but you have to be very careful about other signals. The output from a switch can be guaranteed by making sure that the switch is a changeover type, connected as in Figure 1.3, so that it gives either +5V or zero, in this example. It is important to use a changeover type of switch here, because a digital input must be connected to one of the logical voltages, high or low, and never allowed to 'float'. Many digital inputs, if unconnected or connected

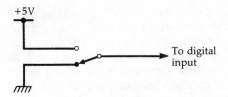

Figure 1.3 Using a switch to ensure that an input voltage is either +5V or 0V

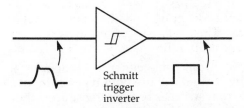

Figure 1.4 A Schmitt trigger inverter, which will convert any input waveform into square waves with very short rise and fall times

to earth through a resistance of a few hundred ohms or more, will take up the higher logical voltage, whether you intend this or not, but the main hazard is that a floating input is easily affected by noise signals.

Where the inputs come from analogue circuits, and do not use a digital-to-analogue converter (DA) IC, then very great care is needed to ensure that the input signals are always of one level or the other. The easier way to ensure this is to make the last stage of the signal processing a Schmitt trigger (Figure 1.4) so as to ensure that any input level to the Schmitt trigger will be converted to the correct level of output.

Level and edge

Some types of digital ICs can be classed as responding to either level or edge inputs, and the difference is important. A device that is described as level operated or level triggered responds to the voltage level of an input signal, and will interpret this voltage as being high or low level. The digital ICs that carry out gate actions are all of this level sensitive type. The alternative is an input that responds not just to the level but to the rate at which the level changes. A device that is described as being leading-edge triggered, for example, will be operated by a sudden change from low-level to high-level. A slow change will have no effect, so that the input is not simply level sensitive, and a change from high to low will similarly have no effect. Conversely, if a device is described as being trailing-edge triggered, this means that it is operated by a sudden change from high level to low. Edge triggering is used in several varieties of the devices that we call flip-flops.

Signal regularity

The signals to a digital circuit can come either at random or at regular intervals, and many circuits will use both types of inputs. If your input signals come from switches or from transducers they are likely to come at irregular intervals when a switch is operated or when the output from a transducer changes. By contrast, if an input comes from an oscillator, the signals will be pulses, the oscillator waveform converted into sharp spikes or square waves, which will be at regular intervals, the time period of the oscillation (Figure 1.5). If the oscillator is a stable one, and particularly if it is a quartz-crystal controlled type, then these regular signals are called clock pulses.

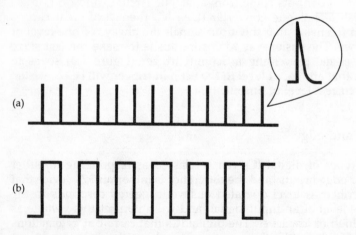

Figure 1.5 Output of an oscillator for digital circuitry can be pulses (a) or a train of square waves (b)

Some circuits that are concerned with monitoring the state of several steady inputs do not need any form of clock pulses. Circuits of this type are called *combinational* circuits, their outputs are determined purely by the combination of inputs that exist at a particular time. You might find clock pulses applied to such a circuit, but their use is not necessary, nor do the ICs have a special clock pulse input. By contrast, the other main class of digital logic circuit is the *sequential* type of circuit. This operates in a sequence, relying on clock pulses to control the timing of the sequence. A circuit of this type will have a separate clock-pulse input, and a signal at another input will have no effect on the IC until there is a clock pulse at the clock input.

Many digital circuits contain a mixture of combinational and sequential ICs, and where a clock-pulse is used you can normally find the clock-pulse oscillator in the circuit, and trace the clock line. In some circuits, the clock oscillator works at a much higher frequency than the circuit can be operated by clock-pulses, and the clock frequency has to be divided down in order to be used. Generating a high frequency at the oscillator allows a smaller crystal to be used, and can allow the divider circuits to generate a frequency which might be difficult or impossible to produce directly from a crystal oscillator, such as 50Hz. Another application of a high frequency clock oscillator is to generate two different clock frequencies which are related to each other, like the line and field frequencies for a TV system.

Signal notation

A very large number of digital circuits are arranged to operate from a +5V supply, but this is by no means inevitable. Battery-operated digital circuits, in particular, will often operate from a 9V battery, or from a car battery whose voltage can range from about 12V to about 14V, depending on whether the battery is discharged or being charged. For that reason, the voltage levels of the digital signals are not normally stated; it is simply assumed that the high level will be close to the positive supply voltage and the low voltage will be near to earth level. The only time when you need to know just what these levels are is when you are connecting one type of digital logic circuit to another. If, for example, you want to send signals from a battery-operated digital circuit in which the levels are +9V and 0V to a mains-operated device which uses +5V and 0V, then some kind of matching is needed. This might not

7

simply be a matter of voltage reduction, as we shall see, because it is possible that the battery-operated circuit might not be able to supply enough current to drive the input of the mains-powered digital circuit if connected directly. Problems like this are solved by using buffer circuits and interfacing.

For the purposes of designing with digital logic, however, the precise voltage levels are unimportant, and we simply refer to them as level 0 and level 1, or more briefly 0 and 1. By using this notation we can also avoid the need to worry about tolerances, provided that we observe the correct operating conditions for our digital ICs. Another important feature of this type of notation is that it allows use to show the action of a circuit by means of a *truth table* in which signals in and out are shown as 0 or 1 levels.

The most important feature of the use of 0 and 1 signal levels, however, is that these are digits. In our ordinary scale of counting, based on a count of ten, these are the first two digits. In the binary scale, more correctly the 8-4-2-1 binary scale, these are the *only* digits. The significance of this starts to appear when we look at digital counting circuits in Chapter 6, but it's as well to lay the framework for the use of binary numbers now, rather than later.

Binary scales

When we count in the normal way, our counting scale uses digits of 0 to 9, and the result of adding one more digit is to make an entry into another column, a tens column. This scheme is extended to having separate columns for hundreds (100 = 10 × 10), for thousands (1000 = 10 × 10 × 10) and so on. Each new column representing an amount of ten times the previous column, is shifted one place to the left. When we write a number such as 7461 we mean 7 thousands, 4 hundreds, 6 tens and 1 unit. This allows arithmetic to be carried out easily, starting with the units column, and carrying a digit over to the next column in addition, or borrowing a digit from the next column in subtraction. The use of this scale, invented by the Moors, is the basis of easy counting, whether for finance, trade or science, and it quickly replaced the old Roman system, in which the letter M meant 1000, C meant 100 and so on. Since the Roman system is not written in columns, even the simplest arithmetic is a very difficult task.

The key to using columns is what each column represents. In the familiar scale of ten, each column represents ten times the value of the column to its right. The column at the extreme right is the units column, and we sometimes refer to this as the *least-significant* column. This is because a digit in the units column is not so important as a digit in the other columns. For example, in the number of 7415, altering this to 7416 is a small mistake, one part in about 7000, but if we altered the 7 to 8, making the number 8415, then the change is one thousand, a very significant difference. The left-most column is the most significant one, the one whose digits represent the largest values.

Each column, then, represents a different multiplier for a digit in that column. For the least significant column the multiplier is 1, unity, and a digit in this column represents the value of just that digit. For the next column along, the value is the digit in the column multiplied by ten, and for the next column, the value is of the digit multiplied by 100. These numbers 1, 10, 100, 1000 and so on are a mathematical series, because we can write 1 as 10^0, 10 as 10^1, 100 as 10^2, 1000 as 10^3 (spoken as ten to the power nought, ten to the power one, ten to the power two, ten to the power three) and so on. The 10^0 is a bit of mathematical agreement—any number to the power 0 is taken to be unity, so that 10^0, 5^0 and 2^0 are all valued at 1.

We are accustomed to counting in tens in this way, but the same scheme can be applied to any system of numbers, and for many purposes it would have been much more convenient if the Moors of old had counted in twelves, since 12 is exactly divisible by 2, 3, 4 and 6, whereas 10 is exactly divisible only by 2 and 5. It didn't work out that way (now if we had 12 fingers, life could have been very different), but the important point is that no matter what number we had settled on as the basis for counting, it could be used in the same way in this scheme of counting in columns. Since we have only two states in a digital logic circuit, and since these two levels are represented by the two digits 0 and 1, we can use the same system of columns also in a number scale which we call *binary*.

The columns don't, of course, represent tens and powers of tens when we are using a binary scale. The first column, the least significant column will use the digits 0 and 1 to represent just these numbers. The next column will be a column of 2's, so that a 1 in this column means one 2. The next column will be a column of 4's (since $2 \times 2 = 4$), and the next will be a column of 8's (since $2 \times 2 \times 2 = 8$). Figure 1.6 shows the multiplier numbers for each column up to 16. The use of columns for numbers that are arranged in powers of two (meaning that each column value is twice that of the column to its right) means that we can use the same method

2^{16}	2^{15}	2^{14}	2^{13}	2^{12}	2^{11}	2^{10}	2^9	2^8	2^7	2^6	2^5	2^4	2^3	2^2	2^1	2^0
65536	32768	16384	8192	4096	2048	1024	512	256	128	64	32	16	8	4	2	1

Figure 1.6 Values of powers of two, showing the value of each column in a binary number

$0 + 1 = 1$
$1 + 0 = 1$
$0 \times 0 = 0$
$0 \times 1 = 0$
$1 \times 0 = 0$
$1 \times 1 = 1$ **Figure 1.7** Elementary laws of binary arithmetic

```
   101101          100100           101011
+  010011        + 010011         + 100110      Addition
 _____          _____          _____
 1000000          110111          1010001
 _____          _____          _____
```

```
    1101             1010            11101
 ×   101          ×   111         ×  1110       Multiplication
 _____          _____          _____
    1101             1010            00000
    0000             1010            11101
    1101             1010            11101
 _____          _____          _____
 1000001          1000110         110010110
 _____          _____          _____
```

```
  110010           101101           100101
-   1010         -   1010         -   1011      Subtraction
 _____          _____          _____
  100101           100011           011010
 _____          _____          _____
```

```
        1001             110             001101
 100⟌100100      101⟌11110        011⟌100111    Division
     100              101               011
     ___              ____              ____
       1             0101              0011
      10              101               011
     100              ___              ____
     100                0             0011
     ___                                011
                                       ____
                                        01
                                       011
                                       011
                                       ___
```

Figure 1.8 The four main arithmetic actions performed on binary quantities, using positive whole numbers

1. Divide number by 2, note remainder (0 or 1) and result.
2. Divide result by 2, note remainder.
3. Repeat step 2 until there is no further result.
4. Write down remainders, starting from bottom.

Example.
Number: 73

```
2) 73  1
2) 36  0
2) 18  0
2)  9  1
2)  4  0
2)  2  0
2)  1  1
    0  ↑
```

read remainders as: 1001001 binary (reading upwards)

Figure 1.9 Converting a denary number into binary by a process of repeated division by 2

1. For each 1 in a binary number, write down the position value from the chart of Fig. 1.6
2. Add these numbers.

Example: 1100110:
$$64+32+4+2 = 102$$

Figure 1.10 Converting a binary number into denary, using the table of powers of two

for binary arithmetic as we use for ordinary scale of ten arithmetic. Instead of counting 1 through 9 to 10, however, we shall count 0, 1, 10, 11, 100, 101 and so on, because there are only the digits 1 and 0, with no digit for 2 just as we have no single digit for ten in our everyday counting scale.

The rules of binary arithmetic are shown in Figure 1.7, and they correspond exactly to the rules of scale-of-ten (which were once taught in primary schools). As with all normal arithmetic, the order of actions is not important, so that 0 + 1 means the same as 1 + 0 if these are pure binary digits (it would be different if 0 meant *right* and 1 meant *left*). All arithmetic is concerned with rules, and when the rules are simple, as they are in this case, then circuits can carry out the actions, and we shall be looking at such circuitry in Chapters 3 and 4. Figure 1.8 shows some examples of the standard processes of arithmetic being carried out with positive binary numbers. Go over these for yourself to be sure that you can see what is being done, and if you are shaky on actions like the borrow in subtraction, then try something similar with ordinary denary (scale-of-ten) numbers to see how similar the actions are. Figure 1.9 shows the conversion of denary to binary numbers, and Figure 1.10 shows the conversion of binary to denary, taking positive whole numbers in each case.

More advanced numbers

NOTE: This section may be omitted when you are reading this chapter for the first time, unless you are reasonably confident with binary numbers. The material in this section will be useful if you are concerned with working with numbers in logic systems, but is not essential to your understanding of the rest of the text of this book.

The numbers that we have been looking at in binary form have all been positive and whole numbers, with no negative signs and no fractions. These are the numbers that we call positive integers. In scale-of-ten, an integer can be of any size, and the only restriction is that the number is a whole number, containing no fractions. When we are dealing with binary numbers in logic circuits, however, we can't have integers of any size, because each digit in a number has to be represented by a voltage level of 0 or 1, and each voltage level has to be stored as a steady voltage on the collector of a transistor or the drain of a FET. In crude terms, there has to be at least one transistor or FET for each digit, and we usually restrict this to some multiple of eight. We deal, therefore, with binary numbers that contain 8, 16, 24 or 32 digits, but seldom with more, and most usually with 8 or 16. The idea that a number can have a limited size because of how we store it is not one that we often worry about in everyday arithmetic, so that this restriction has several important effects in binary arithmetic.

In the examples that follow, we shall look at 8-digit arithmetic because this has been used extensively in the past, is still found, and involves less work than 16-digit or 32-digit work. The principles, however, are exactly the same, so that if you follow what is being done with 8 digits, you can work out for yourself how arithmetic is carried out with 16 digits or more. At this point, too, we can start following the usual convention of referring to a binary digit as a bit, so we are dealing with 8-bit arithmetic.

If we accept that our numbers are worked with in groups of 8 bits, then, what restrictions are placed on us? As the table of Figure 1.6 shows, an 8-bit number can represent the range 0 to 255 (2^8–1). Does this mean that we can't deal with numbers greater than

255 or less than 0? It does if you can only store 8 bits, but you can find two ways round the problem. One is to have more than one store of 8-bit numbers, the other is to deal with 8 bits at a time in the same store, in sequence. We often use a mixture of both methods. We can then use stores the way that we use columns in ordinary arithmetic. One store holds the 8 bits that represent 0 to 255, the next represents the number of units of 256, the number that we get when the first store has been filled once. We can use these 8-bit stores, therefore, as if we were working with numbers in a scale of 256. If you want to hold a 16-bit number, it is immaterial for most purposes whether you hold it in one 16-bit store, or in two 8-bit stores, except that the amount of circuitry needed for two 8-bit stores can be greater.

The important point is that the size of the store is not the most important thing. Using 16-bit stores allows you to deal with 16-bit numbers faster than could be done with two 8-bit stores, but not necessarily *better*. If you design circuits to perform 32-bit arithmetic, the results of the arithmetic will be the same no matter how you organise the storage, as four × 8-bit, two × 16-bit or one × 32-bit. It's the total number of bits per number that counts, not how they are organised. In the examples that follow, we shall assume mainly that this *total* number of bits is 8. This, remember, restricts us to a number range of 0 to 255 at a time.

Now what can we do about negative numbers? There is no negative sign for binary numbers, because all we can represent in terms of electrical voltage are the digits 0 or 1. A negative sign must therefore be represented by one of these digits, and the 1 is chosen for this purpose. We have to know *which* digit is the sign digit, though, and this is always chosen to be the most significant digit, the digit on the extreme left hand side of the set that you are using, whether this is 8, 16, 24 or 32. If this digit is 0, then the number is positive, and if this digit is 1, the number is negative. The scheme looks delightfully simple.

Looks are deceptive, however. Suppose you have a piece of arithmetic like this:

01001101	77 in denary
01000111	71 in denary

10010100	which should be 148 in denary.

in which two numbers are added. There has been a carry into the most significant bit place, however, and when we take this to mean a negative number then it makes the arithmetic incorrect, because

13

adding two positive numbers should not make the answer negative. We can also get an equally ridiculous result sometimes by adding two negative numbers:

10010110	−106 in denary
10001011	−117 in denary

00100001	+33 in denary

and in this example, there has been a carry from the most significant bit (msb), so that the correct digit for the msb is lost. All of this means that using the msb as a sign bit can come unstuck if there is a carry bit into the msb or out of the msb. If the carry out of the msb can be stored separately and not lost, then there are no errors if there is a carry in *and* a carry out in the same addition.

What it boils down to is that when you are working with signed numbers, meaning that the msb is taken to mean a + or − sign, then you can expect trouble if there is a carry into or out of the msb, though things may be normal if both actions occur. Circuits that deal with arithmetic have to be arranged so as to detect these carry actions, and to detect when this situation arises. This is an overflow problem, and the circuits that detect it are overflow circuits. The problems arise because, taking the 8-bit example, numbers from 00000000 to 01111111 are positive (0 to 127 in denary) and numbers from 10000000 to 11111111 are negative (−128 to −1 in denary). Any arithmetic whose result is outside this range of −128 to +127 is overflowing, needing more storage space than is available. You have to ensure in the design of arithmetic circuits that an overflow cannot occur, either by limiting the size of numbers that can be used, by providing more storage space, or by rejecting the result.

This, surprisingly enough, is the only restriction. Using the msb as a sign bit allows the same circuits to be used for arithmetic no matter whether we think of the msb as representing a sign or not. This is the main advantage of the system, and it presents no problem for the circuitry. The problem, as always, is for the human user. We need to look, therefore at how binary numbers can be converted to and from denary when the msb is being used as a sign bit. The numbers must be within the overflow range, and for positive numbers the method is exactly the same as for unsigned numbers. Figure 1.11 shows the methods summarised, with examples.

1. For a positive number in the range 0 to 127, proceed as in Fig. 1.9.
2. For a negative number in the range −128 to −1:
(a) Add +256
(b) Convert result to binary
Negative number examples:
1. −87. Add 256 to get +169. This converts to 10101001
2. −44. Add 256 to get +212. This converts to 11010100

Figure 1.11 Converting numbers into signed 8-bit binary

Fractions

The use of numbers which contain fractions, and numbers which lie outside the normal storage range, presents new problems. For some applications, fixed point arithmetic is acceptable, meaning that a fixed number of storage places can be allocated for a fraction. You might, for example, allocate 32 bits for the whole part of a number, and 24 bits for the fractional part. If you know that the numbers which will be used in a logic system are of a limited range that this type of system can cope with, this is an ideal method, because it is simpler than any other method of dealing with fractions. The bits stored in the fractional part of the store will, of course, be a binary fraction, the binary equivalent of the denary fraction, and Figure 1.12 shows the conversion from denary fraction to binary fraction.

The more usual solution, however, is the use of floating-point numbers. This allows numbers of virtually any size to be dealt with, because the size restrictions are such that even the largest numbers that we use (distances in astronomy) and the smallest (sizes of sub-atomic particles) can be put into this form. The snag, however, is that the use of floating-point representation practically always means that the number is stored in an approximate form.

To see how this system works, it's easier if we use an illustration in denary scale. Suppose we have a number 2576.78 that we want to represent. We can write this in a very different way, as a fraction 0.257678 multiplied by a power of ten, and the power of ten is 4 in this example, because $10^4=10000$ and $10000 \times .257678 = 2576.78$. Another way of looking at it is that the decimal point has been shifted four places, so that we can represent this number as 0.257678 and 4. The fraction is called the *mantissa*, and the 4 is called the *exponent*. A floating point number, or *float*, is therefore a mantissa-exponent form of the number.

Now the problem is that very few numbers can be converted into the form of a binary fraction. The fractions 0.5, 0.25, 0.125 all

Digital signals

(a) Conversion.
1. The denary fraction should not have a zero following the point.
2. The first place of a binary fraction, 0.5 represents ½. If the denary fraction is more than 0.5, write down 0.1 as the binary fraction, and subtract 0.5 from the denary fraction. If the denary fraction is less than 0.5, write down 0.0 as the start of the binary fraction.
3. With what remains, try the next binary fraction, ¼ = 0.25. If the remainder is greater than this, write another 1 in the binary fraction and subtract 0.25, else write 0 and carry on.
4. Repeat this, using the denary equivalents for the binary fractions in (b), until as many places of binary fraction have been used as are allocated.

Example: 0.625
This is greater than 0.5, so the binary fraction starts as 0.1, and we subtract 0.5 from the denary fraction, getting 0.125.
This is less than 0.25, so the next binary figure is 0.
The next denary equivalent is 0.125, so the binary digit is 1, and there is no remainder. This is an exact equivalent, 0.101 binary.
(b) Table of binary fractions.

Binary	0.1	0.01	0.001	0.0001	0.00001	0.000001	0.0000001	0.00000001
Denary	0.5	0.25	0.125	0.0625	0.03125	0.015625	0.0078125	0.00390625

Figure 1.12 Converting a denary fraction into a binary fraction, using the negative powers of 2

convert exactly because they are powers of 2, being 1/2, 1/4 and 1/8 respectively. Any fraction which is not an exact power of 2, however, does not convert exactly, and since all floating-point numbers have to be stored as a fraction and an exponent, this means that there will be conversion errors. No matter how much storage space we allocate, the error will always exist for numbers that are not an exact binary fraction. In denary, we have the same problems of converting fractions like 1/3, 1/9, 1/11 and so on into

Number: 2.8 denary. The whole part, 2 converts to 00000010, and the fraction is found as:

.8 − .5 = 0.3	binary 0.1
.3 − .25 = 0.05	binary 0.11
.05 less than .125	binary 0.110
.05 less than .0625	binary 0.1100
.05 − .03125 = .01875	binary 0.11001
.01857 − 0.015625 = 0.002945	binary 0.110011
.002945 too small for 8 places	binary 0.11001100

Complete binary number is 00000010 exponent and 11001100 mantissa

Figure 1.13 Conversion of a mixed number (whole number and fraction) into a binary fraction (mantisse) and multiplier (exponent)

decimal form. If you need to use numbers in this floating-point form, then, you also need methods of rounding the results when the numbers are converted back, if this has to be done.

To see how much might be needed, consider Figure 1.13 which shows the conversion to floating-point form of the number 2.8, using 8-bits for the mantissa and 8 for the exponent. This, as the example shows, becomes:

00000010.11001100

with the fraction left incomplete because of the limitation of storage. Now if we shift the point to make this:

.10110011

then we have the final form of 8 bits for the mantissa, and the exponent is

00000010

to represent 2 places shift.

This allows the number to be represented in two bytes, but with two sets of approximations. One is the approximation required to represent the fraction in 8 bits, the other is the bits that have been lost when the point was shifted, and the bits following the point were once again limited to 8. Suppose we convert this back now, as in Figure 1.14. This gives 2.796875, and if we work to one place of decimals, this is about 2.8. The error here is 0.003125, and this is just 0.11% of the original number.

These errors can accumulate, however, and will cause problems in working with numbers unless the rounding is well arranged. The problem is mainly one that applies to computing circuitry, and affects the writers of programming languages which handle numbers, but for some digital circuits in which numbers are handled similar problems can be encountered. The errors are greatly reduced if a reasonable number of bits are used for the mantissa, and it is now fairly common to use 32 or 40 bits. Only 8 bits are needed for the exponent, because exponents of 127 or more

Mantissa = .10110011   exponent = 00000010
The exponent signals a two-place shift of mantissa to:
10.110011, for which the whole number part is 2, and the fraction is:
.5 + .25 + .03125 + .015625 = 0.796875

Figure 1.14 Converting a mantissa/exponent binary number back to denary — note the effect of the 8-bit limit to the size of the mantissa

are never needed. The mantissa is a signed number, because the point may need to be shifted right rather than left when a small fraction is being used. A fraction such as .0001101, for example, will be converted to .1101 mantissa and 0000011 (denary 3) exponent by a right shift, and this will be regarded as a negative exponent, −3 rather than +3 in denary terms.

Other codes

The 8-4-2-1 binary code is by far the best for carrying out straightforward arithmetic, and is used almost exclusively in circuitry that is mainly concerned with arithmetic in which no conversion to denary is needed. The 8-4-2-1 type of code is not the only binary code that we can use, however, and several others are likely to be encountered, depending on what type of applications you have for digital logic circuits. One very common variant of the 8-4-2-1 code is BCD, binary-coded decimal. This is a very popular form of coding when numbers have to be shown on LED or LCD displays, because each digit of such a display is one denary digit. In a BCD system, then, each denary digit is represented by 4-bit binary code.

Figure 1.15 demonstrates what this implies. The conversion between BCD and denary is simple, and conversion to a form suitable for driving a display is also simple. The conversion between BCD and binary is, however, not quite so simple for numbers of more than one digit, and arithmetic with BCD is also not so simple. An added disadvantage is that BCD requires more storage space for any given number than 8-4-2-1 binary, though it is possible to devise systems in which number accuracy of floating point numbers can be much better at the cost of very much slower arithmetical processes.

BCD is really just an adaptation of 8-4-2-1 binary, but Gray code is quite a different form. As Figure 1.16 shows, a Gray code scale

Denary number: 258
Convert each digit into 4-digit binary: 2 = 0010
5 = 0101
8 = 1000
so that the complete number becomes 001001011000 in BCD.

Figure 1.15 BCD notation uses a 4-bit binary code for each denary digit of a number. This is more cumbersome than 8-4-2-1 code, but more precise

Denary	Gray Code	Denary	Gray Code
0	0000	8	1100
1	0001	9	1101
2	0011	10	1111
3	0010	11	1110
4	0110	12	1010
5	0111	13	1011
6	0101	14	1001
7	0100	15	1000

Figure 1.16 Gray code and denary. Gray code does not use columns to indicate importance, and is particularly useful for industrial applications that involve the use of transducers

does not follow a pattern of columns, and you always have to use a table to convert a number in Gray code to a denary or a binary 8-4-2-1 number. The Gray code numbers are for 4-bits only, because Gray code is used either in BCD form, or in a scale of 16 (hexadecimal). The advantage of Gray code is that only one bit ever changes at a time during a count up. The change from 7 to 8, for example is from 0100 to 1100, rather than from 0111 to 1000 in 8-4-2-1 binary. This has particular advantages for conversion of quantities like the rotation of a shaft into binary form, because if the shaft is in a position between the angles represented by numbers 7 and 8, then there may be reading errors caused by some binary digits that are changing between 0 and 1, and the fewer digits that change, the lower the chances of error.

There are other forms of binary code, such as Excess-3, which is a form of BCD in which 3 is added to each digit before coding into 8-4-2-1 binary. This means that the smallest value of code is 0011 and the largest is 1100, with anything below 0011 or above 1100 being an error. This makes error-detection easier, and has also the considerable advantage that BCD numbers coded in this way can be manipulated by the same circuits as ordinary binary. The Gray code and the various forms of 8-4-2-1 code are, however, by far the predominant methods of coding that you are likely to encounter.

Logic polarity

Overwhelmingly, modern digital logic devices use positive logic, in which the 1 level is the more positive, and the 0 the less positive. This might mean, for example, that +5V is 1 and 0V is 0, or that

+15V is 1 and −15V is 0. A few systems in the past have used negative logic, in which the more negative level is 1 and the more positive (or less negative) is 0. The use of negative logic is so rare now that it would hardly need to be mentioned if there were not a few negative logic circuits still in use and requiring servicing now and again.

Switch action

The whole of digital circuitry depends on the use of transistors, whether bipolar or FET, as switches working between two voltage levels. The simplest bipolar transistor switching circuit is illustrated in Figure 1.17. When the voltage at input A is 0.5V or less,

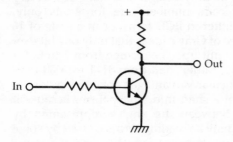

Figure 1.17 The most elementary transistor switching circuit. The circuit is an inverter, giving 0V output for +5V in, and +5V out for 0V in

assuming the use of a silicon transistor, then there is no base current and hence no collector current, so that the collector voltage is high. When the input voltage rises above 0.5V, base current will start to flow, and its maximum value when the input A is at +5V can be regulated by the value of the resistor R1. This resistor value would be chosen so that the dissipation of the transistor would be within safe limits when the input was at +5V.

This type of circuit shows the reason for the tolerances that we encounter in digital logic. The guaranteed 0 voltage is any level from 0 to about +0.5V, and possibly higher, depending on the values of R1 and R2. The guaranteed 1 voltage is any level from +5V down to a value that is also determined by the values of R1 and R2. Fast operation of a switch like this requires the value of R2 to be low, and for currents to be fairly large, so that the resistor

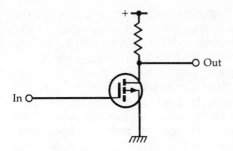

Figure 1.18 The MOS inverter, using a P-channel MOSFET in this example. Only one resistor is needed, since the gate has infinite resistance

R1 will have as low a value as the dissipation of the transistor allows. The problem, however, is that we must make these circuits in IC form, and the fabrication of resistors in IC form is wasteful of space, quite apart from the problems that resistors cannot be formed with close tolerances, and that each resistor will dissipate power.

The corresponding MOSFET circuit is shown in Figure 1.18. This has the advantage that only a load resistor is needed, since no current flows at the input. The input voltage tolerance will depend on the characteristics of the MOSFET, assumed to be an enhancement type, and we can image that it might start to pass current at about 0.7V at the gate. The problem here is that the amplification factor for a MOSFET is low, so that though the MOSFET would be passing maximum current with a gate input of +5V, it is not so easy to predict at what input voltage the output would start to switch over, particularly when we consider the tolerances which inevitably exist in the fabrication of any IC.

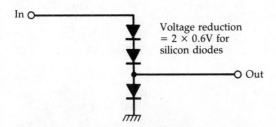

Voltage reduction = 2 × 0.6V for silicon diodes

Figure 1.19 Using diodes in a voltage divider. This is preferable to the use of resistors, since a diode takes up much less space on the IC

The answer is to design switching circuits in such a way as to minimize the use of resistors and the effect of tolerances. The circuits will be examined in more detail in Chapter 2, but the principles are straightforward. Resistors are used only to set quantities such as base current, and an active device is always preferred as a load rather than a resistor. Voltage reduction is accomplished using the voltage drop across a diode (Figure 1.19) rather than across a divider using resistors. The use of an active device rather than a load resistor greatly reduces dissipation, because if one device is on and the other off, the only current that passes is that of the load.

Inputs and outputs

All logic ICs are designed, then, so that for inputs that are within the guaranteed range of 0 or 1, the output or outputs will also be within the guaranteed range. This ensures that the output of an IC can be connected directly to the input of another IC of the same construction so that the guaranteed logic levels will always be maintained. This may not be true if one output has to feed a large number of inputs, particularly if each input passes current. The *fanout* of a digital IC means the maximum number of inputs (of the same IC family) that can be fed with guaranteed levels of signals; a fanout figure of 10 is common. If a greater number of inputs has to be fed (as it often has to be in computing circuits), then buffers (current amplifiers) must be used between the output and some of the inputs.

The speed of response is often of considerable importance, and speeds in the nanosecond range are common. At one time, particularly when the older forms of bipolar transistor circuits were used, fast switching speeds could be attained only when the ICs dissipated comparatively large amounts of power. Modern circuit methods and devices have achieved fast switching with low dissipation, and this has allowed the construction of much more densely packed ICs.

The result of all this is that you can connect digital ICs together into circuits without too much worry about anything other than the logic of the circuit being correct, provided that your power supply is adequate. In general, the limits on fanout have little effect on most logic circuits, and only a few applications are likely to require higher switching speeds than the normal form of digital IC can provide. In many ways, then, the effort spent in design is rather less with digital ICs than with analogue. This obviously does not apply if you are designing something really unusual, but 99% of digital design follows along well-worn paths. Provided you know what you are doing, there are not too many pitfalls.

Power supplies

The power supply for a digital circuit must use some stabilisation, particularly if the faster-switching ICs are used. Some MOS types are intended for battery operation, and this can be completely satisfactory provided that a large value capacitor is wired in parallel with the battery, and smaller capacitors (around $0.1\mu F$) across the + and − supply lines of chips. For mains-powered equipment, a conventional bridge rectifier circuit with large value smoothing capacitors can be followed by an IC regulator, following the maker's recommendations. Do not forget just how much current may be required—supplies of 5V at 10 to 20A are common now for computer circuits, and these are circuits that use low-consumption ICs. The important point is to ensure good decoupling with $0.1\mu F$ capacitors placed between the + and − supply lines either at each chip, if the chips have a high current consumption, or for each 5 chips if the consumption is low.

Though a simple straightforward power supply is adequate, many designers prefer to add a crowbar circuit which will short the supply in the event of a rise in voltage. TTL ICs are susceptible to a rise in the supply voltage caused by the failure of a regulator IC, and the provision of over-voltage protection is a valuable feature, particularly if the logic circuit is an extensive one.

Truth tables

The action of digital ICs is most simply expressed by truth tables, a topic that will be considerably expanded in the following chapter. A truth table has, as its headings, all the input and output terminals of the IC. Every possible combination of input signals can be written down under the inputs, and the output(s) for each combination can be shown. In skeleton form the truth table for an IC with two inputs, A and B, and an output, Q, is:

A	B	Q
0	0	
0	1	
1	0	
1	1	

since there are two inputs, there must be $2^2 = 4$ outputs. It is not necessary to show the inputs in the form of a binary count as shown here, but it is a very useful way of checking that all of the possible inputs have been included. By convention, inputs are usually labelled as A, B, C and so on, with output Q. In this Q column, the various outputs that will be obtained, one for each combination of inputs, can be written.

The truth table is not the only way of describing the action of a circuit, but it is a particularly simple and useful method. We shall be looking at other methods in Chapters 3 and 4, but it's often wise to check with a truth table, particularly since the truth table can so easily be checked in practice, using switches to provide the inputs and a voltmeter or any other indicator to show the state of the output. Truth tables are useful mainly for combinational circuits, and for sequential circuits we need an amended version, the state table, which is examined in Chapter 5.

2 Device types

The inverter

The simplest digital actions are those of the inverter and the buffer. Taking the inverter first, this device is represented by the symbol in Figure 2.1, which also shows the truth table. Unlike a linear inverter, which needs to be able to produce a waveform that is the inverted mirror-image of the input waveform, the digital inverter need only invert the logic signals 0 and 1, giving a 0 output for a 1 input and a 1 output for a 0 input. The action is more correctly described as a NOT circuit (or NOT gate) because the output is NOT the same as the input, it is the reverse. In writing logic, NOT 0 is 1 and NOT 1 is 0 (there isn't anything else in a binary system).

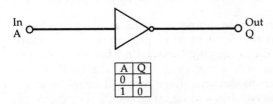

A	Q
0	1
1	0

Figure 2.1 The digital inverter, or NOT gate, and its truth table. Note the circle in the symbol which denotes inversion

The circuits that we looked at in Figures 1.17 and 1.18 are the most elementary NOT gates, and were once obtainable in IC form though their use of resistive loads made the manufacturing processes unsuitable for large-scale integration. Modern methods of manufacturing ICs (and some which are not exactly modern but are still in use) dispense with resistors as far as possible, and use several active components (bipolar or FET) for each circuit type.

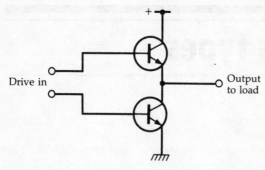

Drive in

Output
to load

Figure 2.2 One common form of output stage for digital ICs, using transistors in series, so that one will be on and the other off except during transitions

The most important feature of the circuitry is that the output stage consists of transistors in series, so that the output terminal will be connected to either positive supply or to earth through one of the two transistors in this series pair. Figure 2.2 shows the principle, which avoids the dissipation in a load resistor, and minimises the dissipation in the transistors, since one will be off and the other fully conducting (with a very low voltage drop) at any given time except during a transition.

Noise margins

Digital circuits are no more immune to noise than analogue circuits, and noise in the form of brief pulses can cause more interference with a digital circuit than with, for example, an analogue audio circuit. The noise margin for a digital IC is the difference between the maximum voltage that will be taken as a 0 and the minimum voltage that will be taken as a 1. For example, if a voltage up to 0.8V is guaranteed to be treated as a 0, and a minimum of 2.0V is taken as a 1, then the noise margin is 2.0 − 0.8 = 1.2V. A noise pulse of 1.2V or more which reaches any input can therefore cause a change in the logic condition at that input if the pulse happens to be in the correct polarity. This may seem quite a large amount compared with the microvolts of noise that are often quoted in linear circuits, but the key point is that digital devices are susceptible to pulse interference. A pulse whose duration is only 25 ns and with an amplitude of just a couple of volts can register as an input for a digital circuit. Such a pulse applied to an audio amplifier would not cause any noticeable effect (unless the amplifier input blocked), and there are not many analogue circuits whose action would be seriously disturbed by such a pulse. By contrast, a digital circuit receiving such a pulse would take it as a valid input, and this could wreck a counting action, or cause a false output; not desirable if your digital circuit controls a robot, your car engine, or your missile defence system.

Interference pulses like this do not necessarily have to arise from outside, either, because each time a digital circuit switches over, there will be a short pulse generated in the power supply line to the IC. This is the reason for connecting a capacitor between the + and − terminals of each IC, because the capacitor will provide the current at the time of switchover, and will then recharge at a more leisurely pace from the power supply. In this way, the power supply voltage does not dip sharply each time an IC switches on. The other line of defence is to make inputs that are of low impedance so that pulses that are radiated or capacitively coupled are greatly attenuated at these inputs. ICs which work with higher voltage levels can have higher noise margins than those which rely on the standard +5V type of supply. If an interference pulse cannot be transmitted through wiring (such as the power line), then it can be transmitted only capacitively or inductively. The use of short connecting strips with no pick-up loops will minimise inductive coupling, and capacitive coupling can be greatly reduced by screening. The use of low impedances at inputs is then a further line of defence to ensure that the amplitude of any interference where it might cause trouble is kept to a very low level.

The non-inverting buffer

The non-inverting buffer is a circuit with a truth table that is almost too simple to print, a 0 in gives a 0 out, and a 1 in gives a 1 out. The symbol is as shown in Figure 2.3−note the absence of the small circle at the output which would mean inversion. A buffer like this serves three main purposes. One is to provide current gain, so that the output of the buffer can supply several inputs of

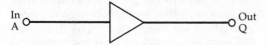

Figure 2.3 The buffer, which serves to restore voltage levels and rise times

other circuits. Another is to provide a low-impedance output, so that signals can be taken along a comparatively long path with low losses and negligible interference. The third purpose is to act as a low-gain voltage amplifier, restoring the amplitude of pulses that have been attenuated in other circuitry.

Buffers are not needed in small-scale digital circuits, because each IC acts as its own buffer. In large circuits, and where circuits are located on several boards with cable connections, or where signals have to be sent to other equipment, buffers are very useful.

Buffer action can be combined with interfacing action. Suppose, for example, that a circuit that operates with a 1 voltage of +5V and a 0 voltage of 0V has to send signals to a circuit in which the 0 voltage is −15V and the 1 voltage is +15V. Clearly the two circuits cannot be directly connected unless the tolerance of the second circuit is so large that 0V will be taken as equivalent to −15, and +5 is high enough to pass as +15. In most cases, some form of interfacing is needed, in the form of a non-inverting buffer whose input will accept 0V and +5V signals, but which operates from a balanced +15 and −15V supply and will deliver these output levels. In this case, the circuit is not simply a buffer but a level-changer as well, a form of *interface*.

Types of circuits

We can't consider digital circuits for much longer without looking at the types of circuits that are put into IC form as digital ICs. Curiously enough, the circuitry that produces the logical effects is not particularly important. The important parts of any digital circuit are the input(s) and output(s), because these ensure that the switching action is fast and of the correct amplitude range. The actual logic can be carried out in various different ways, with diodes or with transistors (even with resistors), and the way that the logic action is carried out has very little effect on the performance of the IC. The real differences start to emerge when we compare and contrast ICs that use bipolar transistors with those that use FETs. At one time, the important difference was speed of switching, with the bipolar transistor notably superior. This superiority still exists, but FET devices are much faster than they used to be. Another difference was that bipolar devices required much greater amounts of current for their action. The difference between the devices in this respect is now less than it was, but the bipolar still tends to use more current.

The most important difference is that FETs can be fabricated in ICs at a very high density, and since they can operate at very low currents these high-density ICs do not overheat when used correctly. FET ICs rule where a lot of logic action has to be crammed into a small space, as in a desk-top computer, but even computer circuits contain a few bipolar devices for actions that cannot be carried out by the low-consumption FETs. Modern methods of IC manufacture are nearing a stage at which both bipolar and FET devices can be made easily and efficiently in a single chip, allowing the FET portion to cope with logic actions and the bipolars to cope with interfacing and buffering.

In the early days of digital ICs, there was a bewildering variety of types of chip, but these have by now reduced to three main types, the bipolar ICs of the TTL family, the CMOS type of FET and the mono-channel FET (PMOS or NMOS). Of those, the original TTL type of chip is almost obsolete, and in general TTL chips are used in small-scale integration only. The CMOS type of chip is found in a logic set that matches the TTL set, and also in some chips for specialised purposes. The NMOS and PMOS chips are used for the construction of microprocessors, memory chips and the various specialised chips for computing purposes. Since the TTL family is still in use, and is found extensively used in older types of logic circuits, we shall start by looking at the various methods that have been evolved for inputs and outputs on these chips.

TTL inputs

The letters TTL are an abbreviation of transistor-transistor logic, distinguishing this type of circuit from the older DTL and RTL systems that used diodes and resistors respectively along with transistors. In the course of the 20 years or so that this family of ICs has been in production, new methods of construction have evolved that use quite radically different operating principles. Nevertheless the TTL family of chips retains one important feature, that the input impedance in the logic 1 state is high and in the 0 state is low. This makes it easy to bias an input into the logic 1 state, and difficult for an interference pulse to change this to a 0 state. Conversely, if an input is held at the 0 state, it will be passing current, and its low impedance inhibits any interference effects. All of the TTL family chips are intended to be run from a +5V

29

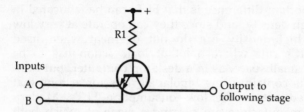

Figure 2.4 The original type of TTL input stage, using a bipolar transistor with multiple emitter contacts. This is a form of common-base stage

single-ended supply, which should be well stabilised and with bypass capacitors for each chip or set of chips.

The original type of TTL input is illustrated in Figure 2.4. This makes use of a transistor which has been formed on the chip with multiple emitter contacts, a multiple-emitter transistor or MET. Each emitter contact is one input for the circuit, which is a form of common-base impedance changer. The base of this input transistor is connected to the supply positive (+5V) through a resistor of about 2K7. When an output connection is at logic 1 (+5V), then no current flows between emitter and base; the transistor is cut-off. When an input is held at level 0, earth, then the value of the base resistor is such that a maximum current of about 1.6 mA can flow. In this state the transistor is fully conducting and the input impedance is low. When more than one input of such a transistor is held at logic 0, the base current is divided among the inputs, and will be less than the maximum value of −1.6 mA. Note the negative sign, which is a reminder that current does not flow *into* the input terminal of a TTL input of this type, but *out* from it.

This input stage by itself is inadequate to perform anything other than a logic action—in the example, this action is of an AND type of gate—and an additional stage is needed between this and any output stage. This is provided by the second transistor which is arranged as a common-emitter stage, with a diode in the emitter circuit to ensure that the base voltage for conduction will be in excess of 1V. The load for this stage is another resistor whose value is not critical, and which will have a fairly high value. With all of the emitter leads of the MET stage at logic 1, no current will flow between base and emitter, and only the collector to base current will flow. This is enough to make the second transistor conduct so that its collector voltage is low. When one or more of the inputs to the MET is low, logic 0, then the main current path in this transistor is base to emitter(s), and there is no current in the base-collector path. This leaves the second transistor cut-off and its collector voltage high.

The action of this input therefore depends on the current that flows between base and collector of the MET to activate the second transistor. This transistor is often operated as a phase-splitter, with a load in both collector and emitter, though the emitter load may be a diode rather than a resistor in some cases. A critical factor in any TTL circuit of this original type is base dissipation. This is controlled by the value of the base resistor and the voltage between supply + and emitter. The maximum base current of 1.6 mA is large by conventional linear standards, so that the transistor is unable to accept much increase in this current value. This implies that the supply voltage should be protected against rising above the maximum that can be tolerated, usually +5.25V. It also implies that a negative pulse at the input should not be allowed to take the emitters to a voltage below zero. This is the purpose of the diodes connected between each emitter of the MET and earth.

Schottky diodes

The use of the MET form of input was the basis of the original family of TTL ICs, known as the 74 family because each type number began with the digits 74, starting with the 7400 gate. The amount of current that flows in each input at logic 0 is quite substantial and though this makes for fast switching speeds in the range of 15–22 ns, the amount of current that flows for logic 0 inputs can be very substantial in a logic circuit that consists of many devices. It is not particularly easy to ensure good stabilisation of a +5V supply at currents of many tens of amperes, and this inhibits the use of standard TTL for large circuits. The current requirements are even higher for the H series of ICs (such as the 74H00) which use lower values of base resistors for even faster switching in the 10ns region.

The fastest switching times are achieved by very different devices, the emitter-coupled logic (ECL) family, but ECL devices are rarely found in circuitry other than specialised military or computer equipment. For most of the applications of TTL logic, the switching speeds are completely adequate, and lower current consumption is of considerably greater importance. The link between switching speed and current was broken by the use of a device that emerged in the 70s, the Schottky diode.

The current that flows in the conventional TTL input is, in fact, not entirely a positive contribution to fast switching speed. When a transistor is saturated, with large values of base current flowing and the collector voltage at about 0.2V above emitter voltage, it can reach a state in which the number of carriers (electrons for the NPN transistor) in the base is large, and will not be cleared out immediately when the bias is reversed. This has two effects—the switching time is increased because of the time needed to clear out the carriers from the base region, and the amount of transient current that has to flow when the bias is reversed can be large. The Schottky diode is constructed using a combination of metal and semiconductor (usually aluminium and silicon), and its most notable feature is a very low forward voltage. A silicon diode has a 0.6V forward voltage for conduction, a typical Schottky diode requires of the order of 0.35 to 0.4V.

Suppose, for example that we have a simple switching stage, connected as shown in Figure 2.5. The Schottky diode (note the symbol) is connected between base and collector and will be

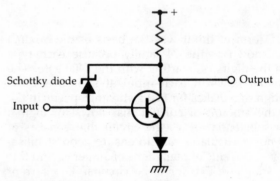

Figure 2.5 Using a Schottky diode between base and collector to avoid base saturation

reverse biased when the collector voltage is high and the transistor non-conducting. When the base voltage is raised, the transistor conducts and the collector voltage is reduced. When the collector voltage falls to about 0.35V less than the base voltage, however, the Schottky diode will conduct, allowing current to flow from the base circuit into the collector circuit and so through the emitter to earth. This prevents base saturation, and makes it much easier to reverse the bias of this stage quickly. An additional benefit is that there is practically no delay in the switching of a Schottky diode.

The use of Schottky diodes in digital ICs was therefore of considerable benefit both from the point of view of permitting low-current operation and for fast switching. It permitted the construction of devices which used much lower currents but which nevertheless provided much the same switching speed as the original TTL types. This series was known as the LS (low-power Schottky) series, and it also permitted the construction of devices with very fast switching (of the order of 5ns) with current values that were not appreciably higher than those of the original TTL types. All of this means that you can find at least four main types listed in a catalogue of TTL digital circuits. The 74xx types are the original 1.6mA 20ns devices, and the 74Hxx are the high-speed versions with greater current demands. The 74LSxx Schottky devices feature currents of around 0.4mA for logic 1 inputs, and the 74Sxx devices use input currents of around 2.0mA for 5ns switching speeds. These types have been available since the mid-seventies, and many manufacturers now add 74ALSxx and 74Fxx series. The ALS series (advanced low-power Schottky) offers reduction in current and in switching speed as compared to the LS type, and the F series offers faster switching action, of the order of 3ns, with a current requirement that is lower than that of standard TTL. These latter types are a development of the older Schottky types.

Schottky diodes can be built-in, during fabrication of transistors, between base and emitter and between base and collector of a transistor, and the symbol that is conventionally used for a transistor constructed in this way is shown in Figure 2.6. In

Figure 2.6 The symbol for a transistor with Schottky diodes incorporated between base and the other electrodes

addition, many Schottky digital devices use Schottky diodes to carry out the logic action, so that in this respect at least they could be classed as being of the diode-transistor logic (DTL) family. Historically, however, all Schottky devices have been taken as being TTL, mainly because they follow the TTL convention of having a high impedance input at logic 1 and a low-impedance input at logic 0.

Schottky inputs

One type of Schottky input is illustrated in Figure 2.7. This uses a bunch of Schottky diodes at the input to the base of an NPN transistor, and this type of input circuit is therefore known as the 'diode cluster input'. The diodes perform the logic action, and the transistor acts only as a switching stage driving the output. If we

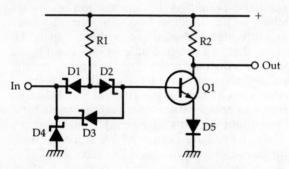

Figure 2.7 A Schottky diode logic stage, followed by a transistor in a logic IC

imagine the input unconnected, the resistor R1 will pass current through D2 to switch Q1 on and make its collector voltage low. With an input at logic 1, diode D1 will be reverse-biased, allowing Q1 to be kept in conduction by the current flowing through R1. At a logic 0 input, D1 conducts, switching the current from R1 through D1 to the input, and using D3 to ensure that the base of Q1 is also brought rapidly to a low voltage. This cuts off Q1 so that the collector voltage rises. The action is of an inverter, and in this example there are Schottky diodes built into the transistor. Because current is being switched at the input rather than voltage this can be a very fast type of switching stage, and more than one input can be catered for by using a separate diode cluster for each input.

Another form of Schottky input is illustrated in Figure 2.8. All of the transistors in this circuit have Schottky diodes between base and collector, and the logic action is carried out by diode clusters. With the inputs held at logic 1, transistor Q1 is maintained conducting by the current through R1, and this current flows in turn into Q3, keeping this transistor conducting so that its collector voltage is low. The connection to the base of Q2 means that this transistor acts as a high-impedance load for Q1, so that the collector current of Q1 is low. When either input is taken to logic

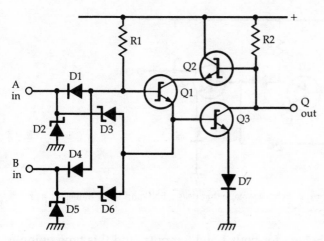

Figure 2.8 A diode cluster and Schottky transistor logic gate

0, the current in R1 is diverted through D1 or D4 (*not* Schottky types), and Q1 is cut-off. This also has the effect of cutting off Q3, and the resulting rise in collector voltage allows Q2 to conduct. The action of Q2 in this circuit is to assist the switchover of Q3. At the instant when the Q1 changes from off to on, Q2 will still be conducting, so that it can supply current to switch on Q3 before it is cut off by the rise in the collector voltage of Q3. It acts as a current booster in this brief instant, and when the change from logic 1 to logic 0 occurs, the high impedance of Q2 at the instant of switching ensures that only the base-emitter current of Q1 has to be switched from Q3. The action of Q2 is sometimes described as 'current kicking'. The diode part of the circuit follows along the lines previously described.

One less usual form of Schottky input is shown in Figure 2.9. This is a complete departure from the other types of input and is found in the faster Schottky types. Transistor Q1 is a PNP type which will be reverse-biased when the input voltage is at level 1. With this input, the collector voltage of Q1 will be high, allowing current to flow into the base circuit of Q2 by way of D2. The Schottky diode D3 ensures that the base voltage of Q2 never exceeds that of Q1 by more than a fraction of a volt, and Q2 cannot saturate because of its built-in Schottky diodes. When the input is at logic level 0, Q1 conducts heavily, so that Q2 is cut-off. The input voltage cannot fall substantially below zero because of the presence of D1. The unusual feature of the circuit is that the input

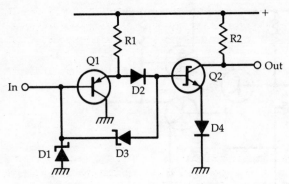

Figure 2.9 A form of Schottky stage that uses a PNP and NPN transistor pair

impedance is high for both 1 and 0 inputs, and this type of input is found mainly on buffer stages for which it is an advantage to have the least possible loading of the circuit that drives the buffer input. For a buffer, only one input per buffer is required as shown here.

One point that is common to all Schottky inputs is that an input must never be left disconnected, floating. It was possible with the early TTL types when low-speed logic actions were being performed to leave some inputs unconnected, when they behaved as if connected to logic 1. This was always bad practice, because it made such inputs very susceptible to noise interference, and it is totally unacceptable when the inputs are to Schottky devices. All logic inputs must be connected in one of three ways:

1   To the output of another working logic device
2   To the +5V supply, possibly through a resistor
3   To earth, directly, with no resistor in series

and care should be taken to avoid connection to earth through a series resistor, which is almost as bad as a floating input unless the resistor is of a very low value. A floating input is at high impedance, and because Schottky devices use much lower current levels than older TTL types, an interference pulse can easily cause a brief switch from 1 to 0. The prohibition on a resistor in series with a logic 0 connection arises because of the current that flows to earth from an input at this voltage. The presence of a voltage drop across a resistor will raise the 0 level voltage, making the noise immunity that much less and endangering the correct operation of the circuit under interference conditions. A digital input that is to be driven from discrete transistor circuitry should never be fed from a conventional single emitter-follower, since this makes the impedance to earth too large. A compound NPN/PNP emitter-follower (like the audio output totem-pole circuit), or a straightforward output from a collector with a low-value resistor load can be used satisfactorily.

TTL outputs

The output stages that can be found in TTL ICs are just as varied as the input circuits, but practically all feature the use of two transistors in series. Figure 2.10 shows a very common pattern in which Q1 is called the high level driver and Q2 the low level driver.

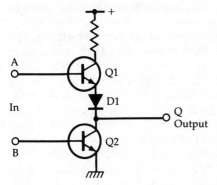

Figure 2.10 The simplest form of TTL output stage, using two transistors in series along with a diode

The circuit will always be driven by a phase-splitter stage to ensure that only one of the two transistors conducts at any given time, other than during a switchover period. This is a simple circuit, using a minimum of components and with a very low power consumption. When the output level is high, Q1 is conducting, and the output level will be about 1.2V lower than the supply voltage, because of the base-emitter drop of Q1 (about 0.6V) and the diode drop of D1, also of about 0.6V. This lowers the noise-immunity of the output. A resistor can be connected externally, however, to raise this logic 1 voltage, and because of the presence of the diode, the voltage can even be raised by this 'pull-up' resistor to a level above the supply voltage. There is nothing to

37

prevent this level from being raised to +7V or more (given a suitable supply voltage) so that the output from the TTL circuit can be used to drive CMOS or other MOS circuitry working with higher logic levels. For a logic 0 output, Q1 is cut off and Q2 is fully conducting. This allows current to enter the output terminal and flow through Q2, with a voltage level of about 0.2V. The only disadvantage of this circuit is that it cannot charge a capacitive load so quickly as some others, because in a transition from 0 to 1, current has to be supplied through both a transistor and a diode, and the diode is the limiting device. In this, like other output stages, the base of the high driver will be connected to the + supply through a resistor or transistor while this transistor is on, and the low driver will have its base earthed to hold it off. When the voltages reverse, the high driver will have its base voltage held low by being connected to a transistor collector or emitter, and the low driver base will be driven from the emitter of another transistor.

Figure 2.11 shows another form of circuit which uses a Darlington connection for the high driver. The high driver is in

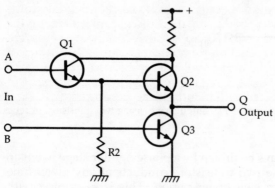

Figure 2.11 A Darlington form of TTL output stage

many respects the more important from the point of view of circuit improvements, because it is always more difficult to charge stray capacitance from 0 to 1 than to discharge it (which can be done by using a single conducting transistor). The low driver can make use of the low voltage drop across collector to emitter, but the high driver, unless complementary transistors are used, is always a form of emitter-follower. This restricts the high voltage level to around 0.6 below the level at which the base of the high driver can be maintained, and correspondingly restricts the rate at which capacitance can be charged. This makes it useful to be able to connect an external pull-up resistor or to make use of the input of a gate connected to this output to act as a pull-up. The output level can be pulled well above +5V if needed for interfacing.

In the Darlington circuit shown here, the maximum output voltage is normally +3.8V because of the drops across the two base-emitter junctions. With the main current flowing through just one transistor, however, charging stray capacitance can be rapid, and the comparatively low logic 1 voltage can be attained reasonably quickly. An external pull-up resistor can be used, as it will reverse-bias Q2, allowing the voltage level to reach +5V, or higher if the resistor is connected to another supply. The noise immunity is no better than that of the transistor-diode stage and the power dissipation is higher because two transistors are conducting at the logic 1 state, with one dissipating through a resistor.

Figure 2.12 shows another version of Darlington design for the high driver. In this case, the resistor load in the emitter of Q1 is returned to the output terminal, and this allows the output voltage to reach +4.4V at logic 1, because with no current flowing, there is no voltage drop across R2 and the final output voltage is the voltage at the emitter of Q1. There is, however, plenty of current available during the transition from 0 to 1 because of the current gain in Q1 and Q2. The output voltage can be raised by using an external pull-up resistor, but not above +5.6V because the resistor that is shown connected to the output also has, in its IC form, a

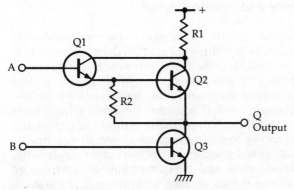

Figure 2.12 A second form of Darlington output stage

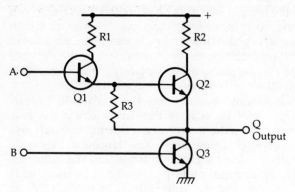

Figure 2.13 A double emitter-follower type of output stage

'stray' diode connection to the supply line. The circuit can be constructed very compactly in IC form because Q1 and Q2 share a collector.

The version of Figure 2.13 uses a two-stage emitter-follower, and gives an output voltage in the logic 1 state of +4.4V which once again cannot be pulled higher than about 5.6V because of a 'stray' diode across the resistor. This is a problem of using a circuit diagram to represent the action of an IC, because an IC contains so many 'invisible' or 'stray' components of this type. The double emitter follower has an additional disadvantage of requiring more elaborate construction.

Three-state circuits and open collectors

Many types of digital circuits, particularly the more elaborate types, are described as being 'three-state'. This does *not* mean that a third logic state is used, and the third state is a 'floating' output state with both high and low driver transistors cut off. In this isolated state, the output terminal(s) can be taken high or low without current passing, and this allows devices to have their outputs connected together. Normally,the outputs of digital ICs should not be connected together, because if one device has its high driver conducting and another has its low driver conducting, very large currents will pass, and the output voltage level will be indeterminate until one device or another burns out. By making use of a three-state capability, the circuits can be arranged so that

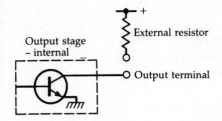

Figure 2.14 An open-collector output which allows outputs to be connected in parallel without risk. This is a form of OR gate, see later

only one output at a time is active. This is required most often in computing circuits where several devices have their outputs connected to a common set of lines (a bus) and can place signals on to the bus when enabled.

An older solution to the problem is illustrated in Figure 2.14, in the form of an open-collector output stage. The IC is constructed with no form of load, and only one output transistor. This allows several outputs to be connected together, sharing an external load resistor, so that when none of the outputs is conducting, the resistor will pull the voltage up to logic 1, and if any one or more than one output stage conducts, the level will be reduced to logic 0. This arrangement is often referred to as a 'wired OR', since the logic 0 level is reached when one OR more outputs conducts. The arrangement is almost obsolete now because the output impedance is high at the logic 1 output, an external load resistor is needed, and the rise of voltage is comparatively slow, since it depends on the value of the external resistor.

MOS devices

MOS digital circuits make use of MOSFETs, using P-channel, N-channel or a mixture of both. The inputs to circuits of this type will always be to the gate of a MOSFET, which has a high impedance in any state, and the outputs can use circuits that are constructed very similarly to TTL outputs. A peculiar advantage of MOS construction, however, is that because the current required at an input is negligible, the logic stage and output stage can be the same. This is a saving of devices, and since a MOS device can be manufactured to take up very little room on a chip surface, this

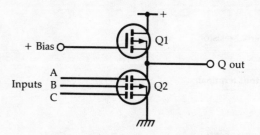

Figure 2.15 A multiple-gate MOS circuit for logic use. Current flows only when all three gates allow conduction, making this an AND logic

type of construction is used extensively for large-scale integration, in which several hundred thousand devices may be formed on one chip.

MOS logic circuits can make use of multiple gates, as Figure 2.15 shows. In this diagram, Q1 is a conventional P-channel MOSFET whose gate is returned to a fixed bias voltage, which can be obtained from a diode chain. The logic stage is Q2, which uses three gate electrodes, all of which must be turned on if current is to pass. When all three gates are at a low voltage, with the MOSFET cut off, the bias on Q1 will ensure that the output is at logic 1, and will allow a small current to pass from the output terminal if this is needed. When the three gate electrodes are all at a voltage above the FET turn-on voltage, Q2 can pass current, lowering the output voltage. How low this can go depends on the ratio of the impedances of the FETs, and this in turn depends on the ratio of channel length to channel width (the *aspect ratio*) for each FET. Those quantities will have been determined in the design of the chip so that the low voltage at the output is lower than the turn-on voltage for the following input.

Logic can then be determined by the input arrangements, and Figure 2.16 shows the two main types, illustrated by P-channel devices. The common factor is the use of another biased MOSFET as a load. In (a), the input stages are in parallel, so that biasing either or both devices on will cause the output voltage to drop to zero. The circuit in (b) requires both inputs to switch the FETs on in order to pass current and reduce the output voltage. These two circuits provide the OR and AND type of logic, and a plain series pair of devices will provide for inversion.

The logic levels of MOS devices are not necessarily the same as those of TTL, even when the devices are operated from the same

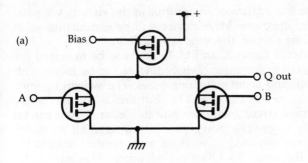

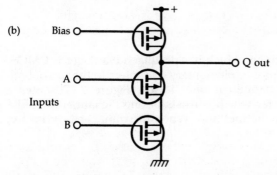

Figure 2.16 (a) An OR gate action (NOR in this example) using separate MOS devices. The output is low for either A or B high. (b) A form of AND (NAND in this case) in which the output is low only if A and B are both high

power supply level. In general, it is possible for the logic 1 level of a MOS output to be closer to the power supply level than that from a TTL circuit when no pull-up resistors are used, but the logic 0 voltage of a MOS circuit is not usually as low as that of its TTL equivalent. Logic 0 levels of around 0.4V are often found in computing MOS circuits, but if output stages of the types used in TTL are also used for a MOS circuit, then the logic levels can be very close to the levels of the supply voltage and earth levels. The greater the supply voltage, the greater the noise immunity of the circuit, but the high impedance of the inputs would make them very susceptible to pulse interference if they were allowed to float. Each MOS input must therefore be connected to a suitable logic level either directly or through a very low value of resistance. An input which is connected to another MOS output is adequately protected by the impedance of the output in the circuits we have looked at so far, since one MOS device will be conducting at all times, and the other when the logic level is low.

The use of NMOS rather than PMOS tends to be favoured for large-scale integration, because NMOS devices can be made with lower dissipations and faster switching times. The switching times are not usually as low as those of TTL, but this is not inevitable, and MOS switching circuits with times of the order of 10ns can be constructed. For large-scale integration, however, MOS digital devices are usually required to work at more modest speeds for which times in the range 80–120ns are adequate. This allows the use of simpler circuits of which more can be fitted on a chip.

CMOS

One form of MOS circuit which has peculiar advantages is CMOS, in which the C means complementary and refers to the use of both N-channel and P-channel in one device. Figure 2.17 shows a typical CMOS inverter which consists of one P-channel MOSFET in series with an N-channel one. When the input voltage is low,

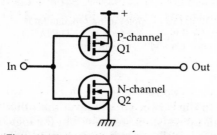

Figure 2.17 A typical CMOS inverter circuit, using a P-channel and an N-channel FET in series

the N-channel FET Q2 is cut off, but the P-channel FET is fully conducting. This makes the output voltage high, almost equal to the supply voltage. When the input voltage is at level 1, the P-channel FET is cut off, and the N-channel FET conducts to ensure that the output voltage level is very close to zero. The logic actions can be obtained in the same way as described for NMOS or PMOS above, by using series or parallel connections of the FET pairs in this example. A notable feature of any CMOS arrangement is that the input is always to a complementary pair.

Though the input impedance of any MOSFET is always very high, the noise immunity can be high, because most CMOS circuits can be operated with a +15V supply. Provided that no inputs are left floating, the immunity to interference pulses can then be better than that of TTL. The early CMOS chips were slow, with switching speeds of around 100–120 ns, but later types have been developed with much lower times, of the order of 10 ns. This has led to the development of a family of CMOS ICs bearing the same type numbers as the familiar TTL types, but with the advantages of much lower dissipation for the same switching speeds, and logic levels that are much closer to the supply voltages.

CMOS chips are used almost exclusively for very low-consumption circuits, particularly for battery operation. The very small current requirements mean that circuits can be kept permanently connected in some cases, so that computer memory chips can be backed-up with a battery to ensure that their contents are not lost when the mains power is turned off. Similarly, it is possible to use chips in programmable calculators which will retain programming instructions for many years until the battery fails. In microcomputers, the use of CMOS is confined to portable machines, because for desktop machines, the demand for more speed and more memory increasingly rules out CMOS, particularly since there are no CMOS equivalents of some of the 16 and 32-bit microprocessors that are now in use.

Fanout and other features

No matter what type of IC construction is used, there are common features of digital chips that have to be considered for design purposes. One of these is fanout, meaning the maximum number of inputs that can be connected to and driven from a single output of the same family. For example, a Schottky LS TTL input requires a maximum current at level 0 of 0.4 mA, and the output of a similar chip will deliver (source) a maximum current of 4.0 mA. In the worst possible case, then, a single LS TTL output could drive up to 10 LS TTL inputs and still maintain guaranteed logic levels. It is likely that a greater number could be driven, but the important point is that the guaranteed number, the fanout, is 10, and if you choose to drive a larger number you cannot expect the chip manufacturer to be sympathetic if your circuit fails at any time. A

45

fanout of 10 is standard for TTL chips, but this assumes that identical chips are being used. If a standard TTL chip, with a guaranteed minimum current output of 16 mA is driving LS inputs, each of which requires a maximum of 0.4 mA for logic 0, then the fanout will be 40 rather than 10, and conversely if an LS output is used to drive standard inputs, a fanout of 2 is more appropriate.

Fanout is more difficult to define for MOS chips, because there is no input current requirement for MOS inputs. For very slowly-changing signals, the fanout of a MOS circuit (PMOS, NMOS or CMOS) is almost infinite, but this is not true for the type of signals that will be used. Each time a MOS output (or a TTL output, of course) is switched, stray capacitances in the circuit, together with any load capacitance, will have to be charged or discharged, and this action requires current to flow through the MOS devices. The greater the switching speed, the greater the transient current that must flow, and the fanout for a MOS device is therefore determined by the switching speed that will be used. The higher the switching speed, the lower the fanout figure, and the manufacturer of the MOS ICs will provide the data on the relationship. In general, a fanout of 10 or more at the normal switching speed is to be expected.

All digital circuits make use of protection diodes, but MOS circuits have more need of protection to prevent voltage spikes from reaching the gates, and for protection against electrostatic voltages generated during handling. These diodes are easy to put in place during manufacturing, in fact it would be difficult to avoid putting some of them in place, so that it is most unusual for a MOS circuit to be affected by handling or by interference. Some of the devices, such as earthed copper manacles, that were fitted to operators working with MOS chips are used now only for operators working in the manufacture and testing of chips, and for most users only the most rudimentary precautions, such as earthed soldering irons and anti-static matting, are needed. Most users can, in fact, handle an MOS chip with complete confidence in this respect. Unless you get a shock each time you walk over the carpet and touch an earthed radiator, it is unlikely that handling a MOS chip will cause any problems.

3 Gates-elementary analysis

A gate circuit, or *combinational* circuit, is one whose output is determined totally by the combination of inputs at the gate. As those inputs change, the output will change, following the logic rule for that gate, whatever it may be. The action of the gate will be the same no matter what form of construction is used. Gates are the fundamental building-blocks of digital circuits, just as transistors (bipolar or FET) are for linear circuits. The action of a gate can be described in several ways, one of which is the truth table as outlined in Chapter 1. In this chapter we shall look both at truth tables and at other ways of describing gate action.

The simplest form of gate that is ever described as a gate is the inverter or NOT gate, whose symbol and truth table have been dealt with. Though this is a very simple device, its action bears out very important points about gates in general. The output level, for example, is determined *entirely* by the input level; it must be 0 or 1, and it can be 1 only when the input is 0 and 0 only when the input is 1. This is an essential feature of any combinational circuit, and one that is noticeably absent from the other main class of digital circuits, the sequential circuit. The importance of gates is that the simple gates can be used to make complex gating (combinational) circuits and also to make sequential circuits, and sequential circuits can in turn be used to make memory circuits, so that the whole range of digital circuits depends on the construction and use of gates.

AND and OR gates

The AND gate symbol and truth table is shown in Figure 3.1. The symbol that has been used is the international one, since that will

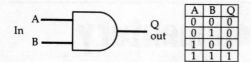

Figure 3.1 AND symbol and truth table for a 2-input gate

be the symbol used in manufacturers' data sheets and in almost all circuit diagrams. Candidates for some UK examinations (C&G and BTEC) are compelled to use the British Standard logic symbols which are illustrated in Appendix A. These symbols are very seldom seen or used outside the examinations context.

The example of AND gate that has been illustrated here is a 2-input gate, and the truth table for the action of a 3-input gate, along with the symbol is illustrated in Figure 3.2. The number of lines

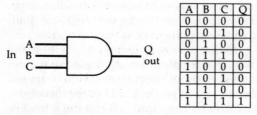

Figure 3.2 Symbol and truth table for a 3-input gate. Only one line of the truth table gives a 1 for Q

for a truth table is 2^n, where n is the number of inputs, but though the truth table is a good way of showing visually the action of the gate, most of its lines are redundant. It is simpler to focus on the one condition that is important, the one which gives rise to a 1 at the output, and this allows us to state the action of the gate as giving a 1 output only when all inputs are at 1. This statement is true for an AND gate with any number of inputs, so that when you write a truth table for a gate, always concentrate on the action that gives the 'odd' result. Some designers describe a logic 1 output as simply an *output*, so that the AND gate provides an output only when all inputs are at logic 1.

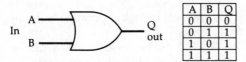

A	B	Q
0	0	0
0	1	1
1	0	1
1	1	1

Figure 3.3 The OR symbol and truth table

The OR gate is shown in symbol form and truth table, for two inputs, in Figure 3.3. Once again, the action leads to one line that is different from the other three, but this time it's the line that gives a 0 output, a NOT 1 output. The gate action is that the output is 1 if any one or more inputs is at 1, so that you should have no trouble in writing a truth table of 8 lines for a three-input OR gate. Notice the symmetry of the truth tables for the 2-input AND and OR gates. The AND gate gives its exceptional line when all inputs are 1 and the output is 1; the OR gate's exceptional line is when all inputs are 0 and the output is 0. There are logical connections between these two, as we shall see later.

How would we use these gates? Figure 3.4(a) shows an AND gate being used to switch a set of digital pulses on and off, using the setting of a switch. The advantage in this type of circuit is that the switch, with its long leads and its stray capacitance, has no contact with the fast pulses that are being switched, it acts only on one input of the AND gate. This is using the word gate to mean the same in digital terms as it does in linear terms. Figure 3.4(b) shows a similar 2-input gate used to operate a LED only when two switches have been put into the ON position. This is the basis of many types of safety interlocks in which an action is possible only

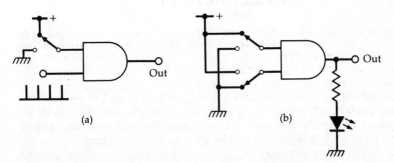

Figure 3.4 Using an AND gate (a) to switch pulses on and off, (b) to give an output for only one setting of two switches (a combination lock action)

49

when a combination of setting is achieved. Gating in this sense is the electronic equivalent of a combination lock, operating only for one particular combination of inputs.

The inputs need not all be ON inputs, because inverters can be used to convert a 0 signal into a 1 before applying it to a gate, so that combinations like 10110 can be used—if we imagine a five-input gate, the circuit would require two inverters. Timing is also important. The output of a gate is 1 only if the inputs are 1 all at the same time. This can be a very useful method of detecting when two signals arrive together, or finding by how much time they overlap.

The OR gate opens up more possibilities, because it can be used to combine inputs. Suppose, for example, that we wanted to use a switch so that in one position it would pass one signal, and in the other position would pass another signal, with no signals passing through the switch. Figure 3.5 shows one solution. This

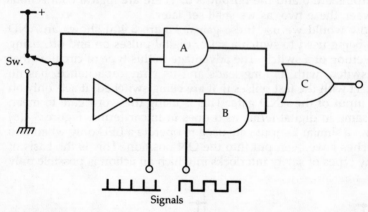

Figure 3.5 Gates in a selection circuit, so that the output will be one signal or the other depending on the switch setting. Note that the switch does not handle any fast-changing waveforms

circuit uses one inverter, two AND gates and an OR gate. When the switch delivers the 1 level, gate A is on, and will pass the pulses to the OR gate, C. This will give the pulses at the output, because each 1 input to an OR gate gives a 1 output. When the switch is reversed, gate A shuts off, but because of the inverter gate B receives a 1 and passes the other pulse train to the OR gate. Again, the OR action ensures that the pulses appear at the output.

The AND and OR gates, along with the inverter or NOT gate, make up the simplest theoretical gate types. For practical purposes, though, it's easier to manufacture and often easier to make use of gates that combine AND or OR with NOT in one gate. Such a gate is the NAND gate, illustrated in Figure 3.6. You can see from the truth table that the action is a combination of AND followed by NOT, so that the output is 1 unless all of the inputs are 1, when the output becomes 0. We can also make a NOR gate (Figure 3.7) in which the output is 1 only when all inputs are 0, falling to 0 when any input is 1. These gates are easier to provide because of the inverting action of a transistor, bipolar or MOS, which ensures the NOT action. If we want to make strict AND or OR gates, then we have to use another inverting stage in the IC. Since the NAND/NOR type of gates are more useful than the apparently simpler AND/OR types, they take a much more prominent place in lists of logic ICs.

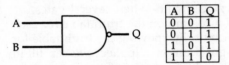

A	B	Q
0	0	1
0	1	1
1	0	1
1	1	0

Figure 3.6 The NAND gate and its truth table. Note the small circle indicating inversion at the output

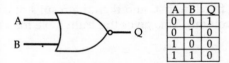

A	B	Q
0	0	1
0	1	0
1	0	0
1	1	0

Figure 3.7 The NOR gate and its truth table

The most important point is that because a NAND or a NOR gate includes the NOT action, it can be used to carry out any gate action, given a suitable circuit. The simplest example is the use of a NAND or NOR gate for the NOT action. Figure 3.8 shows two ways in which this can be done for a 2-input NAND gate. In (a), one input is connected permanently to level 1, so that the voltage level on the other input gives the truth table as illustrated. In (b), both inputs are connected together. Either way, you can compare these truth tables with the full truth table for the NAND gate and

51

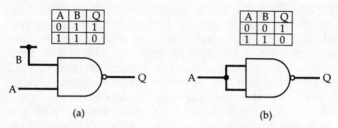

A	B	Q
0	1	1
1	1	0

A	B	Q
0	0	1
1	1	0

(a)   (b)

Figure 3.8 Using a NAND gate as an inverter (a) by connecting one input to level 1, (b) by paralleling the inputs

see that these are simply extracts from that table. Try it yourself for a NOR gate.

To show that the NAND gate (or NOR gate) can be used to provide other gate actions needs some consideration of how we draw up a truth table for a gate circuit. When several gates are connected together, we need a column on the truth table for each gate input, and one for the output. By knowing the truth table for the first gate to which the signals can be supplied, we can fill in part of the table. These signals in turn are applied to another gate, and knowledge of this truth table allows another set of columns to be filled in, until the final output is reached. Figure 3.9 illustrates this for a simple example using a NAND gate followed by another NAND gate connected as an inverter. The column for the output of the first NAND gate, C, is filled in first, and then the results of inversion are put into the Q column. This gives the truth table for an AND gate, as expected.

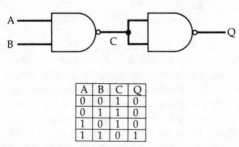

A	B	C	Q
0	0	1	0
0	1	1	0
1	0	1	0
1	1	0	1

Figure 3.9 Inverting the NAND output to produce the AND truth table, used to illustrate how to build up a truth table for a circuit

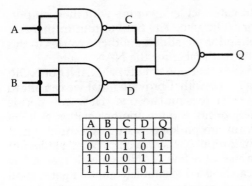

A	B	C	D	Q
0	0	1	1	0
0	1	1	0	1
1	0	0	1	1
1	1	0	0	1

Figure 3.10 A circuit containing three NAND gates, and the truth table built up by labelling the intermediate outputs and including them in the table

Now try a rather different one. Figure 3.10 shows a circuit in which each input, A and B, is inverted before being applied to a NAND gate. The truth table for columns C and D can be filled in at once from the inverter action, and then the Q column is completed knowing that C and D are inputs to a NAND gate. The final output Q is the OR of A and B, so that this circuit, made up from three NAND gates, gives the logic action of an OR gate. If we took the Q output of this circuit and inverted it, we would have the output of a NOR gate.

The same types of transformation can be carried out using NOR gates. Following a NOR gate with an inverter gives the truth table for the OR gate as you might expect. The circuit of Figure 3.11 shows the NOR gate equivalent of the circuit of Figure 3.10, in

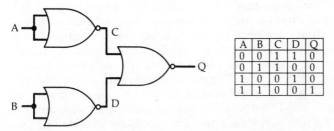

A	B	C	D	Q
0	0	1	1	0
0	1	1	0	0
1	0	0	1	0
1	1	0	0	1

Figure 3.11 A circuit containing three NOR gates, showing that this gives the effect of an AND gate

53

which the first two NOR gates act as inverters with their outputs being applied to another NOR gate. The final output in this case is that for an AND gate, and if we added another inverter to this output, we would get the truth table for the NAND gate.

What it all boils down to is that one gate type, NAND or NOR, can be used to substitute for any other provided that we can afford to use several gates in order to simulate one. How you decide whether to do such a thing or not is quite another matter. A lot of gates that come in IC form are packaged as quad 2-input gates, meaning that you get four 2-input gates on a chip. In a logic circuit, you might find that the use of a few NAND gates leaves a few unused gates and these can be used to simulate another gate action so that it would not be necessary to add another gate type. You do not necessarily set out to simulate every gate type with NAND or NOR, and in some cases it would not make sense to do so. Very often, however, you find that most of your logic actions can be carried out by using NAND or NOR gates mainly, and if you need the odd AND or OR, then simulation makes sense. The main aim is to keep the lowest number of chips, the chip count, whatever methods you use.

The XOR gate

The action of the OR gate is not what we usually mean in everyday language by OR. When we say 'one or the other' we usually mean to exclude the case of both, but the OR gate includes this, so that it gives a 1 output when both inputs are 1's. Because of this, it's useful to have a chip that carries out the exclusive OR action, the XOR gate. The symbol and the truth table are shown in Figure 3.12.

Now can we create this action from a set of other gates? The answer, as you might expect, is that we can, but not quite so easily. Figure 3.13 shows one circuit which will carry out the action, along with the truth table. The inputs are applied to two gates in parallel. One of these is a straightforward OR gate, the other is a NAND gate. The output from the OR gate is in column C, and the output of the NAND gate is in column D. Now you can see that if we AND these C and D outputs, we get the result that we want, the truth table for the XOR gate. This circuit could be amended further to be built entirely from NAND or NOR gates. Also, as we'll see later, this is not the only way of constructing an XOR gate.

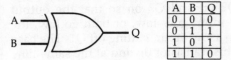

Figure 3.12 The XOR gate symbol and truth table

A	B	Q
0	0	0
0	1	1
1	0	1
1	1	0

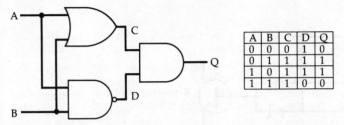

A	B	C	D	Q
0	0	0	1	0
0	1	1	1	1
1	0	1	1	1
1	1	1	0	0

Figure 3.13 A gate circuit which carries out the XOR action, using an OR, an AND and a NAND gate

Gate circuits

Apart from inverters, the NAND and NOR type of gates are the simplest to construct. Figure 3.14 shows a NAND gate constructed with Schottky diodes and transistors. The bare minimum of transistors is needed here—the logic for the inputs is carried out by the diodes, the transistor Q1 acts as a phase-splitter and the conventional TTL type of output is used. With both inputs high,

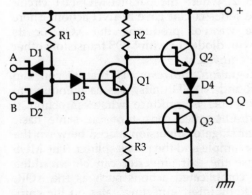

Figure 3.14 Internal construction of a NAND gate using Schottky circuits

55

Q1 is biased on, turning Q2 off and Q3 on so that the output voltage is low. When either input goes low, or both go low, the current through R1 diverts to a low input, cutting off Q1. The base voltage of Q2 rises turning this transistor on and at the same time Q3 turns off, so that the output is high, the action of the NAND gate.

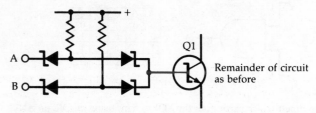

Figure 3.15 A modification to the input of the previous circuit allows it to be used as a NOR gate

Quite a small change in the circuit produces the version in Figure 3.15, which gives the logic of a NOR gate. This time each input is separately biased by a resistor, so that when the current of one resistor is diverted, the other resistor continues to hold Q1 conducting. In this way, Q1 is not cut off until both inputs are together held at logic 0, and this is the NOR-gate action. These two examples show that the fundamental actions of NAND and NOR require only a small number of components, and this component count is even lower when the MOS circuits are used, as was demonstrated in Chapter 2, where the parallel MOSFET circuit gave NOR action and the series circuit gave NAND action. There is, however, no simple way of producing the XOR or its counterpart, the XNOR, with diodes or with MOS transistors other than by forming the gate equivalent.

The advantage of integration, however, is that if you can produce the simple NOR and NAND units, it is easy enough to connect gates internally so as to produce whatever action is required. The AND and OR gates consist of the same basic structure but with another stage of inversion placed between the diode logic of the bipolar example and the phase splitter. The MOS example is easier, because the extra inverter can be an added output stage. The more complicated actions such as the XOR, however, have to be made by interconnecting gates on the chip, and this was one of the first applications of the integration of gate circuits as distinct from using integration to create gates. The TTL series of gates does not use integration on a large scale, and a typical TTL chip would contain four gates or eight inverters rather than a complete digital circuit. This is because TTL circuits are by their nature of fairly high dissipation, and for large scale integration lower-power dissipation systems must be used. These need not necessarily be FETs, and at one time it looked as if integrated injection logic (I^2L) might be used, but FET technology certainly dominates the larger scale of circuitry.

Another point is that the construction of logic circuits using TTL or MOS chips from families such as the 74 set and the CMOS 4000 set is useful mainly for development work and small runs of production. Using FET techniques, it is possible to construct large arrays of gates and inverters on the surface of a chip, but with no interconnections made. These interconnections can be designed, and then added to the chips to form custom-designed large-scale circuits. The action of the complete circuit can be checked by computer (and the interconnections designed by computer), so that the user can be confident, if the specification has been adequate, that the circuit will operate correctly. This method has replaced the use of large circuits using TTL or CMOS chips for logic purposes, but mainly in computers rather than in industrial electronics.

Boolean logic

One of the things that makes so much of engineering possible is that almost every new branch of engineering can make use of mathematical techniques that were developed years, sometimes centuries, earlier. Logic is the science of drawing conclusions from facts and at one time was taught extensively. Logic, like electrical science, is based firmly on a few rules, and these rules, unlike the rules of electricity, have been known for several thousands of years. Throughout most of that time, however, the rules had been expressed in words and were not necessarily easy to apply.

This was all changed in 1854 by a mathematician called George Boole. He was interested, as are all mathematicians, in rules, and he wondered if the rules of logic could be reduced to mathematical forms. Don't, by the way, confuse mathematics with arithmetic. Arithmetic is the everyday use of numbers that we need for counting, mathematics is an abstract study, a search for rules that might or might not ever have any applications. Boole thought that logic could be reduced to rules by making use of the idea that each part of a logic problem could be true or false, and that by using some system of rules on all these true or false parts, the whole problem could be solved. He decided to use the digits 1 for true and 0 for false, so making use of a binary code (not entirely new), and wrote out the logic actions that he thought would be needed to solve all logical problems.

Note, by the way, that I say *logical* problems. A logical problem is one for which all the facts are known, and their effect on the problem is also known. Many real-life problems are not so simple, because we might not know all the facts, or be sure which of many facts have any bearing on the problem. These may be matters for investigation and trial, and only when the rules are known can we start to make use of logic methods. Very few problems that concern human behaviour, including economic behaviour, can be analysed using logical methods because humans often respond to what they believe rather than to the facts that they might know. Like sheep, we prefer to follow a leader rather than try to find a logical path of our own.

Boole concluded that the fundamental rules that were needed were those of the AND gate, the OR gate and the NOT inverter, as he had found that other possible requirements, such as the XOR action, could be derived from combinations of the other rules. Boole, remember, did not know of anything corresponding to gate circuits; electrical circuitry was in its infancy, but his conclusions were of immediate interest to engineers who were working with switching circuits. They were also of interest to railway engineers who were working on safe signalling systems, because railway signalling is a process that should be totally run by the rules of logic. A statement such as 'if the points are set to the branch line or the gates are open to the road then set the mainline signal to stop' is one that can be reduced to the action of an OR gate, though in the early days of signalling these were mechanical actions. The signal levers are keyed or gated by cross-bars, and it's well worth a trip to an old signal-box to see just how complicated mechanical logic can be—and how well the engineers of a century ago could design it.

All that we have looked at so far concerning gate actions and truth tables, then, was devised by and understood by Boole and a few engineers and mathematicians in the middle of the 19th century. The next step that Boole made was to liberate the rules of logic from the clumsy truth tables. As we have seen, most of a truth table is redundant, because in most gate actions only one line of the truth table gives rise to a different output. Boole proposed to use symbols for the basic gate actions, and then to work with combinations of gates by manipulating these symbols. Any form of working with symbols rather than numbers is called algebra (a word from Arabic, reminding us that most of our science has had Arabic origins), so that this particular very useful branch of mathematics is called Boolean algebra.

Take, for example, the simple 2-input AND gate, with inputs A and B and output Q. The Boolean description of this action is:

$$A.B=Q$$

which in words is A AND B gives Q, reminding you that Q is 1 only when both A and B are at 1. For a three-input gate with inputs A, B and C, the rule is:

$$A.B.C=Q$$

read as 'Q is 1 when A and B and C are all at 1'. The important points here are the use of the dot to mean the AND action, and the way that the action is written as an equation.

The same can be done for the OR gate, and for this action, Boole used the + sign. The action of a two-input OR gate is therefore written as:

$$A+B=Q$$

read as 'Q is 1 when A or B or both are at 1', and the three-input gate can similarly be written as:

$$A+B+C=Q$$

in the same way. This is where you need to be careful, because in ordinary everyday terms, the + sign is associated with addition, and often with the word 'and'. This makes it difficult to read + as OR, but it's a habit that you have to acquire if you are to make any headway with Boolean algebra.

Why should you use Boolean algebra? The answer is because it's short and neat, unlike truth tables. You can always check the action of a logic circuit using truth tables, but it's likely to take considerably longer and you can't always be sure that all of the circuit is really pulling its weight. The methods of Boolean algebra are quicker, neater, and will reveal unexpected problems, like gates that are wired in the circuit but which do not contribute to the logic. Boolean algebra is an extremely useful method of finding a suitable gate circuit to carry out the action of a truth table, since the design of a digital circuit generally starts with the truth table that has to be implemented. In addition, if you are working on the servicing of a logic circuit, you can expect to find that the action will be described in terms of Boolean algebra rather than by using a truth table. The truth table for a circuit with a large number of inputs and outputs would be a vast one, and by no means easy to work with or to check. A description in Boolean algebra can be brief and still show all the working of the circuit. The difference is rather like the difference between a circuit diagram and the practical layout—it's a lot easier to follow the circuit diagram once you know what the symbols mean.

There is one more Boolean logic symbol that we need, the symbol for inversion, the NOT action. This uses a bar above a letter, so that if the letter A means that A=1, then $\overline{A}$ means not 1, equal to 0; A=0 then $\overline{A}$ means not 0, equal to 1. The bar can be placed over a complete set of logic actions, so that:

$$\overline{A.B}$$

means NOT (A AND B), and is the Boolean way of writing the NAND gate action. We can also write:

$$\overline{A+B}$$

which is the NOR gate action, and the bar can also be placed over other combinations that have been placed within brackets, like

$$\overline{(A+B).(C+D)}$$

meaning that the result is NOT [(A OR B) AND (C OR D)]. For the moment, though, we'll stick to the simpler equations or expressions. Any combination of letters that uses the . and + signs, with or without bars, is called a Boolean algebra expression, or just an expression.

So far, all we have is a set of symbols that makes it simpler to write down a logic action for which we already know a truth table. The rules so far are just the rules that we know from the truth tables, and the symbols are a convenient shorthand. Before we can make more serious use of Boolean algebra, we have to know how these symbols of . and + and the bar can be manipulated, and this takes some working at, plus experience.

First of all, we have to find out if there are any similarities between Boolean algebra, and the older methods of ordinary algebra. Just to take a very simple example, is A+B identical to B+A, and is A.B identical to B.A? You would expect this to be true, and a quick check with the truth tables confirms this, but you always have to check these things when you come across them first. The quantities A and B which will be signals that can be 0 or 1 are described as being commutative, meaning that the order in which they appear in an action (as A.B or B.A.) is unimportant.

Now suppose we have three digital signals, A, B and C. Can we be sure that:

$$A+(B+C)=(A+B)+C$$

and that

$$A.(B.C)=(A.B).C$$

and once again, checking with truth tables confirms that this must be true. Once again, though, you will find that the use of truth tables is very clumsy. An easier method is to represent each quantity by a switch that can be open(0) or closed (1). The AND (.) action is then represented by switches in series, and the OR (+) by switches in parallel. Figure 3.16 shows the switch combinations that correspond to these two equations.

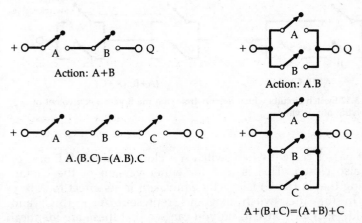

Action: A+B

A.(B.C)=(A.B).C

Action: A.B

A+(B+C)=(A+B)+C

Figure 3.16 Using switches to represent gate actions, and show that arrangements of quantities in brackets in a Boolean equation is immaterial

The next thing that we might expect of algebraic quantities is that they should be associative. This means that the equations:

$$A.(B+C)=A.B + A.C$$

and

$$A+(B.C)=(A+B).(A+C)$$

might be true. The first of these is true in ordinary algebra where the dot means multiplication and the + means addition, but is it true for digital gates? The second is certainly *not* true for ordinary algebraic quantities in which the letters represent ordinary numbers.

Both, however, are true for Boolean quantities, as you can see from the switch diagram in Figure 3.17. In the first case (a), the

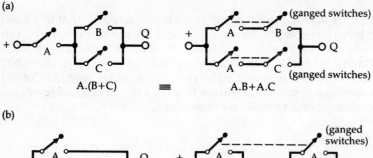

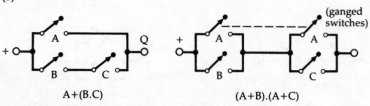

Figure 3.17 Switch circuits which demonstrate that the Boolean equivalent of 'multiplying out' is valid

circuit passes current when switch A is closed and either B or C or both also closed. This is true for either version of the circuit, showing that A.(B+C) is exactly equivalent in its effect to A.B + A.C. In (b), the switch diagrams represent A + (B.C) and (A+B).(A+C) and once again you can see that these are identical from the point of view of switch operation. If you are still in any doubt, try the long way round and draw up truth tables.

This illustrates that you cannot take a new algebra for granted. Boolean algebra is, in this sense, more associative than ordinary algebra in which equations such as A + (B.C)= (A+B).(A+C) are definitely not true. If you doubt this, try putting in numbers like:

2 + (3.4) = (2+3).(2+4), meaning 14 = 30

to see how completely false this is. This is yet another reason for making a special effort to remember that the + means OR and the

. means AND, so that you will remember that these equations *are* true for Boolean algebra.

Another simple equation is:

$$\bar{\bar{A}} = A$$

meaning, in words, that NOT NOT A is A. The double-negative cancels in Boolean algebra, just as it does in correct English (where *I didn't do nothing* means *I did something*).

There are several other equations that we can prove are true for Boolean algebra but which are not true in ordinary algebra. These equations look strange on paper, but sound perfectly reasonable when you remember the Boolean meanings of . and +. The first is:

$$A + A = A$$

which means that A OR A is just A. This is just two of the lines of the OR truth table, 0 OR 0 = 0 and 1 OR 1 = 1, when we try it out with A=0 and with A=1. By the same methods, we can see that:

$$A.A = A$$

meaning that A AND A is A, the equivalent of 0 AND 0 = 0 and 1 AND 1 = 1.

If these look strange at first sight its because you are still thinking in terms of ordinary numbers, for which $A+A = 2A$ and $A.A = A^2$. Once you remember to translate . into AND and + into OR, then the statements start to look perfectly reasonable.

There are another two equations, each involving an inverse quantity. The first is:

$$A + \bar{A} = 1$$

meaning that A OR NOT (A) is 1. If A is 1, then NOT(A) is 0; and if A is 0, then NOT(A) is 1. Either way, one of the two must be 1, and by the laws of OR, 1 OR 0 is always 1.

The other equation is:

$$A . \bar{A} = 0$$

meaning that A and NOT(A) is always 0. Once again, this is just a statement of part of the AND truth table, because if A=0, then NOT(A)=1, and if A=1 then NOT(A)=0. Either way, 0 AND 1 is always 0 by the rules of the AND gate.

Given these rules, summarised in Figure 3.18, how do we go about writing the action of a gate circuit in Boolean algebra? The straightforward gates. OR, AND and NOT, have been converted

1. $A+B = B+A$ and $A.B = B.A$
2. $A+(B+C)=(A+B)+C$ and $A.(B.C) = (A.B).C$
3. $A.(B+C) = A.B + A.C$ and $A+(B.C) = (A+B).(A+C)$
4. $A + \underline{A} = A$
5. $A + \overline{A} = 1$
5. $A.A = A$
7. $\underline{A}.\overline{A} = 0$
8. $\overline{\overline{A}} = A$ Note that $\overline{A.B}$ is not identical to $\overline{A}.\overline{B}$ nor $\overline{A} + \overline{B}$ to $\overline{A + B}$

Figure 3.18 A summary of the rules of Boolean algebra

already, using the three basic symbols of Boolean algebra. The question now is how we describe actions like NAND and NOR and XOR in Boolean terms. Once we have taken these in, we can start on the conversion of more elaborate digital circuits into the form of a Boolean equation.

Taking the NAND gate first, its equivalent, in terms of AND and NOT, is the AND gate followed by the NOT gate, so that the logic is NOT(A AND B). This means that the Boolean equation is:

$$\overline{(A.B)} = Q$$

using the brackets to show that the NOT action is on the result of A AND B, not on A or B individually. Boolean algebra uses the brackets in the same way as conventional algebra, to indicate priority. Whatever is enclosed in the brackets is always worked out first, before any other actions outside the brackets are applied. If you have one set of brackets inside another, the innermost brackets have top priority, then the outer brackets, then anything else. The usual convention of labelling the output as Q has been used.

In the same way, the NOR gate action is written as:

$$\overline{(A+B)} = Q$$

meaning that A OR B is worked out, and then the inverse taken. The immense advantage of using Boolean algebra is that it corresponds so well with the gates that are used to implement it. The equation above indicates an OR gate followed by an inverter, which is what the NOR gate is.

Now for the real test—how do we write an XOR gate? Perhaps a quick reminder of the XOR truth table will help here. This is shown in Figure 3.19(a), with its first three lines from the OR truth table and its last line from the AND truth table. One way of converting this into Boolean equation form is to look at the OR truth table, and what we would have to do with the output of the OR truth table to get the output for XOR. We can see from Figure

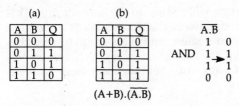

(A+B).$\overline{(A.B)}$

Figure 3.19 The XOR truth table (a) and how ANDing an OR truth table output with suitable quantities can give the desired output. This leads to a gate expression

3.19(b) that if we ANDed each output with a quantity that was 1 for the first three lines and 0 for the last, we would get to the XOR truth table. The quantities that need to be ANDed here, however, are the lines of a NAND gate, so that what is needed is:

(A OR B) AND (A NAND B)

which is written in Boolean terms as:

(A+B).$\overline{(A.B)}$

That's the same solution to the problem as we looked at earlier, but it's not the only one. Boolean algebra allows us to come up with another equation for the XOR gate action, one that still requires the same gating actions, but which looks simpler and which can be reduced to rules.

To do so, we concentrate on the middle lines of the XOR truth table, the lines that yield a 1 answer. One line is A=0, B=1, and the other is A=1, B=0. Now

A=0, B=1 is $\overline{A}.B$ and A=1, B=0 is A.$\overline{B}$

so that we can write the output as:

Q = $\overline{A}.B$ + A.$\overline{B}$

which must therefore be true for the lines that give 1 as their output. What do we get for A = B = 0? The answer is that since 1.0 = 0, the answer must be 0. For the condition, A = B = 1, then the same applies, each term is 0.1 and the answer is 0. This much simpler looking statement therefore describes the action of the XOR gate in Boolean terms.

Now comes the real test. If we have two Boolean equations which both seem to describe the XOR gate, and which certainly give the same truth table as the XOR gate, then these two equations ought to be equivalent, and we should be able to show that the more complicated one will reduce to the simpler one. This depends on Boolean algebra following the same rules as conventional algebra when it comes to dealing with sets of quantities that use the dot and the + signs. In conventional algebra, remember, these have different meanings, of multiplication and addition respectively. The expression

$(P + Q) . (X + Y)$

can be multiplied out to give:

$P.X + P.Y + Q.X + Q.Y$

and if you doubt this, Figure 3.20 shows the action with numbers in place of letters.

$(P + Q).(X + Y) = (P.X + P.Y + Q.X + Q.Y)$
$(2 + 3).(4 + 5) = 5.9 = 4.5$
$2.4 + 2.5 + 3.4 + 3.5 = 8 + 10 + 12 + 15 = 45$
(remember that . means multiplication in conventional algebra)

Figure 3.20 A reminder of how multiplying out brackets works in ordinary algebra, with the same action in numbers to show that it is valid

Conventional algebra is a way of working with numbers in the form of symbols, and Boolean algebra is a way of working with logic actions in the form of symbols, so we might expect that the two would not necessarily follow the same rules. As we have seen, however, this type of action is the same in Boolean algebra, so that we can work on the expression:

$(A + B) . \overline{(A + B)}$

as if this were a multiply-add type of equation.

This means that we can 'multiply out' to get:

$A.\overline{A} + A.\overline{B} + B.\overline{A} + B.\overline{B}$

which does not yet look like our alternative expression. There are, however, in this expression, two redundant parts. We have seen already that each of the terms

$A.\overline{A}$ and $B.\overline{B}$

must always be 0, so that they need not form part of the equation. This leaves the result as:

$A.\overline{B} + B.\overline{A}$

which we know is the same as

$$A.\bar{B} + \bar{A}.B$$

since order does not matter in Boolean algebra. This is the second form of the XOR gate equation, the one we derived by considering the 1 lines of the truth table.

For many purposes, the following set of steps illustrates the best way of getting from a truth table to a Boolean equation.

1 Write the lines of the truth table that give a 1 output
2 If input A is 1, then write it as A
3 If input A is 0, then write it as $\bar{A}$
4 OR these expressions together, and simplify as needed

The action of simplifying Boolean equations requires the use of a few more points than we have looked at so far, but we can gain some experience for the moment in writing Boolean equations. Note incidentally, that the form of the XOR gate that we have obtained in this way is shown in Figure 3.21. This requires two AND gates and one OR gate, along with two inverters, and is, if anything, more difficult to construct than the earlier version that used the OR, AND and NAND. The simplest Boolean equation does not guarantee the simplest practical construction, mainly because we prefer to use NAND and NOR, and Boolean algebra works with AND and OR. Intelligent use of Boolean algebra, however, can show how to make an action work and then how to make it work with gates that are convenient for you.

Now look at a fairly simple gate circuit. Figure 3.22. This has three inputs, labelled as A, B and C, and it uses three gates, a NAND, a NOR and an AND. What Boolean equation can we get from this, and what does this circuit do? Remember that to find

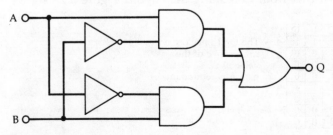

Figure 3.21 A form of XOR gate circuit that uses five gates

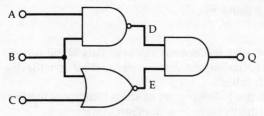

Figure 3.22 A gate circuit for analysis by both truth table and Boolean methods

the truth table for the circuit you can always work directly, but in this example, we'll work from the circuit.

Start with the action of the NAND gate, which is:

$$\overline{(A \cdot B)}$$

and the action of the NOR gate is

$$\overline{(B + C)}$$

then these two are ANDed to give:

$$Q = \overline{(A \cdot B)} \cdot \overline{(B + C)}$$

and we can take breath here. Just writing this makes it a lot easier to see what this circuit will do, because the main parts are connected by an AND, so that Q = 1 only when both of the ANDed quantities are 1. Now the first of those,

$$\overline{(A \cdot B)}$$

will be 1 for anything except A=1, B=1, and the second part:

$$\overline{(B+C)}$$

will be 1 only for B=0 and C=0.

This means that to get Q=1, we can have B=0, C=0 and A=0 or A=1, and this implies that the A input is redundant. Would you have known that from examining the circuit? Figure 3.23 shows

A	B	C	D	E	Q
0	0	0	1	1	1
0	0	1	1	0	0
0	1	0	1	0	0
0	1	1	1	0	0
1	0	0	1	1	1
1	0	1	1	0	0
1	1	0	0	0	0
1	1	1	0	0	0

← The Q=1 lines occur irrespective of the value of A, so that gate A is redundant

Figure 3.23 The truth table analysis of the circuit—note the size of the truth table

the truth table, obtained from the circuit itself in the usual painfully long way. This bears out that the condition B=0, C=0 is the important one and that the A input does nothing for the logic. From the Boolean expression, we can get to this result more quickly and, once you know the ropes, more easily. In the following chapter, we will look at two further rules that make it possible to work out the redundancy of the A input in this example without even having to consider truth tables.

Now what of the problem that is a familiar one when you are designing a logic circuit. You know what the truth table has to be, but you are not sure of how to implement such a truth table. This is where Boolean algebra is at its most helpful, because it provides a way that will always lead to a working gate circuit, though you still have to use your cunning and experience to make this gate in the form that will be most economical to you, using whatever gate chips you have most readily available.

A	B	C	Q
0	0	0	0
0	0	1	0
0	1	0	0
0	1	1	1
1	0	0	0
1	0	1	1
1	1	0	1
1	1	1	1

Figure 3.24 A truth table for which a gate circuit is required. This is a 'majority voting' type of truth table

Figure 3.24 shows an example of a truth table. This is of a 'majority verdict' circuit, one that gives a 1 output when two or more of its inputs is at 1, a useful principle for redundancy engineering. Following the rules that we laid down earlier, we seize on the lines that give a 1 output, which are when:

B=1, C=1 or A=1, B=1, or A=1, C=1 or A=1, B=1, C=1

and we put this into Boolean terms. This makes the conditions read as:

$$Q = (A.B) + (B.C) + (A.C) + (A.B.C)$$

and we can at once draw up a gate circuit that will carry out this action, shown in Figure 3.25. This requires five gates, and the obvious question is, can we simplify the action? We certainly can,

Gates–elementary analysis

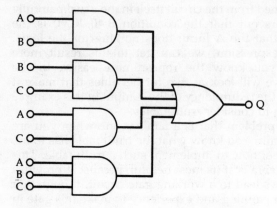

Note: Gate inputs shown as A, B, C rather than as wired connections

Figure 3.25 A gate circuit derived from the Boolean expressions taken from the truth table

A.B + B.C + A.C + A.B.C	Original expression
B.(A + C) + A.C.(B + 1)	Re-grouped
but B + 1 = 1 and A.C.1. = A.C	
B.(A + C) + A.C	Result

Figure 3.26 Regrouping and simplifying the Boolean expression

but not to one unique answer. We can produce several gate circuits which will carry out the action, and we can choose for ourselves which is most convenient. For the moment, it's best to stick to just one solution. Figure 3.26 shows the steps, showing that it ends up with:

A.C + B.(A + C)

which can be carried out by the gate circuit in Figure 3.27. This is an improvement, using two AND gates and two OR gates only so that we could construct two such majority voting circuits with two ICs, one quad AND gate and one quad OR gate. As we shall see in the following chapter, there are also other ways of analysing the circuit. We have, for example, gone for the lines that gave the 1

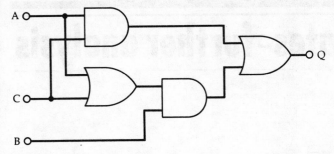

Figure 3.27 The gate circuit that carries out the logic of the simplified equation

output. We could just as easily have gone for the lines that would give a 0 output, and write these as giving the NOT Q result.

This would give us:

$$\overline{Q} = \overline{A}.\overline{B}.\overline{C} + \overline{A}.\overline{B} + \overline{A}.\overline{C} + \overline{B}.\overline{C}$$

so that NOT Q = 1 for these various combinations. We won't pursue this for the moment except to note that it can be a useful way of getting equations into forms that can be solved by using NAND and NOR gates rather than by AND and OR. Before we can work extensively with Boolean equations, however, we need to know two more equivalences, and also another method of finding which parts of an equation are important and which are redundant.

4 Gates–further analysis

The circuit in Figure 4.1 consists of two OR gates and an AND gate, and is suspected to be more than is required to carry out the action. We start an analysis by writing the Boolean equation, which is:

$$Q = (A + B) . (B + C)$$

and then we can 'multiply out' this expression, to give:

$$A.B + A.C + B.B + B.C$$

and we can start to simplify and then gather the terms that we have here. To start with, B.B simplifies to B, since 0 AND 0 is 0 and 1 AND 1 is 1. We can then regroup (the equivalent of factorisation in ordinary algebra) in the form:

$$A.B + A.C + B. (1 + C)$$

and the term (1 + C) can go out, because 1 OR C must simply be 1. We are now left with:

$$A.B + A.C + B$$

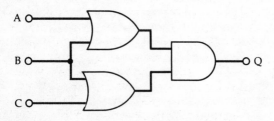

Figure 4.1 A gate circuit for analysis

and we can regroup this as:

A.C + B. (1 + A)

and once again remove the 1 OR A term, leaving:

B + A.C

so that the circuit action could be carried out by one AND gate and one OR gate, as in Figure 4.2. You can draw up the truth tables for these two circuits to check that they are identical.

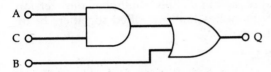

Figure 4.2 The simplified version of the circuit

Karnaugh mapping

Not everyone has a taste for the sort of algebraic manipulation that this first example uses, and there is an alternative method, called Karnaugh mapping, which can be used to simplify Boolean expressions. Karnaugh mapping involves drawing a form of short truth table from which redundant parts can be eliminated by using a set of simple rules. It looks rather like a game of noughts and crosses in action, and, for anyone who is perplexed by the groupings and eliminations of the algebraic method, it can offer an alternative that can be easier for gate circuits with not too many inputs. A Karnaugh map for a circuit with three inputs is relatively simple, for four inputs it is more difficult, and for more than four inputs you need hot tea and aspirin.

The principle is to draw up a form of truth table which will have a box for each possible term in the Boolean expression. These boxes are arranged in rows and columns, and for a three input circuit, there are four rows (one for each possible state of two inputs) and two columns (one for each state of the remaining input). A blank Karnaugh map for three inputs therefore looks as in Figure 4.3. What you have to watch carefully is the order of the AB quantities. This does not follow a binary count, its order is 00, 01, 11, 10 reading downwards, a Gray-code sequence. Depart from this

	C	
AB	0	1
00		
01		
11		
10		

Figure 4.3 A blank Karnaugh map for a circuit with three inputs

order, and you will find yourself in trouble! To make use of this table, you need the expression in its fully 'multiplied out' version, consisting of a set of quantities that are ORed together. In the example we looked at, this is:

A.B + A.C + B.B + B.C

and we can use this to give a 1 or set of 1's for each term, so placing four 1's into the Karnaugh map. The first term is A.B, meaning that for the position where A=1 and B=1, we can place a 1. Since C does not appear in all this, we can place a 1 in both columns for the A=1, B=1 line (the 11 line), as shown in Figure 4.4.

	C	
AB	0	1
00		
01		
11	1	1
10		

Figure 4.4 Placing 1's into the Karnaugh map to represent the A.B term

This is done for each term in the equation. The A.C line will place a 1 in the C=1 column and the A=1 rows, and since there is a 1 in the A=1, B=1, C=1 box already we do not need to put in another. The B.B expression puts a 1 for each box where B is 1, regardless of the values of A or C – once again, some of these boxes are already filled in. The B.C term then puts 1's in where B=1 and C=1, and we find that these boxes are already filled. When you find that there is overlapping like this, it's a sure indication that there is quite a lot of redundancy in your circuit. For each box which does not contain a 1, you can now place a 0, Figure 4.5, though this is not strictly necessary.

74

AB	C 0	1
00	0	0
01	1	1
11	1	1
10	0	1

Figure 4.5 Completing the Karnaugh map with 1's and 0's

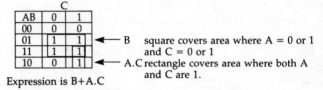

Expression is B+A.C

B square covers area where A = 0 or 1 and C = 0 or 1

A.C rectangle covers area where both A and C are 1.

Figure 4.6 Marking groups of 1's on the map, and assigning the meanings of B and A.C to these rectangles

The next crucial stage is the selection of the wanted parts of the map which are, in this case, the boxes that contain 1's. What we are interested in is a line or box of 1's, and in this example we can find three lines of them, as illustrated in Figure 4.6. The biggest number we have collected together and unbroken by any 0's is the set of four in the A=0, B=1 and the A=1, B=1 rows. The common factor here is B=1, so this line represents a term B. The odd 1 out can be linked to the one above it, true of C=1 and A=1, so that it represents A.C. This makes the simplest expression B + A.C, as expected.

Suppose we represent the majority voting circuit of Figure 3.24 in this way. The Boolean equation was:

A.B + B.C + A.C + A.B.C

and this gives the Karnaugh map which is shown in Figure 4.7. In this example, there are no sets of four, and the best we can do is to mark one set of three and one of two, as in Figure 4.8. The set of two is in the line where A=1, B=1, so this is a term A.B. The vertical line of three occurs where we have C=1 and either A or B at 1. This is a term C.(A + B), so that the complete expression is:

A.B + C.(A + B)

C

AB	0	1
00	0	0
01	0	1
11	1	1
10	0	1

Figure 4.7 The Karnaugh map for the majority voting truth table

C

AB	0	1
00	0	0
01	0	1
11	1	1
10	0	1

← A.B

↑ C.(A+B)

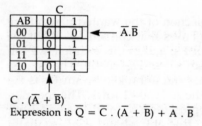

Figure 4.8 The groups of 1's marked out to yield an expression

C

AB	0	1
00	0	0
01	0	1
11	1	1
10	0	1

← $\overline{A}.\overline{B}$

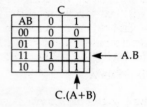

↑ $C\,.\,(\overline{A} + \overline{B})$

Expression is $\overline{Q} = \overline{C}\,.\,(\overline{A} + \overline{B}) + \overline{A}\,.\,\overline{B}$

Figure 4.9 The Karnaugh map for the majority voting truth table with the 0's marked so as to form the expression for NOT Q

Now we can look at another way of getting simplified Boolean expressions. We mentioned in Chapter 3 that it might sometimes be an advantage to get an expression for NOT Q rather than for Q, since this might yield an expression that would allow the use of NAND/NOR gates. The Karnaugh map makes this type of thing very simple, because it requires only that we concentrate on the 0 lines rather than on the 1 lines.

As an example, Figure 4.9 shows the majority voting circuit mapped out again, but with the 0 lines marked. There appear to be three sets of zeros in this, but in fact we can reduce the sets to two. The easy set is the line for AB=00, and this represents the state:

$$\overline{A} . \overline{B}$$

because the zeros appear where we have NOT A and NOT B, the AB=00 line. The other set is less easy. We might think of the column for C=0 with AB=00 and AB=01 as being a pair of zeros, with an odd one in the bottom line of the C=0 column. This would be perfectly valid, but it can be simplified further by thinking of this odd zero as being part of the upper two. You can think of the table as being wrapped round a cylinder so that this zero is in line with the other two — the rule is that each box is surrounded by four other boxes, and the boxes at the edge are no exception. When you mark out, this joining of boxes at opposite edges is indicated as shown, by making loops with open ends.

The result of this is that this set gives the logic expression:

$$\overline{C} . (\overline{A} + \overline{B})$$

since the zeros occur in the C=0 column when either A or B is zero. This makes the complete expression:

$$\overline{Q} = \overline{C} . (\overline{A} + \overline{B}) + \overline{A} . \overline{B}$$

and later we shall look at ways (the De Morgan theorems) of simplifying this further. The important point is that if you draw up a truth table for NOT Q and with another column for Q, you will find that the Q column is exactly the same as it was for the original majority voting circuit.

The principle of 'joining round the corner' is further illustrated in the circuit of Figure 4.10, for which the Boolean expression is:

$$Q = \overline{A}.\overline{B}.\overline{C} + A.\overline{B}.\overline{C} + A.B.\overline{C}. + A.\overline{B}.C + A.B.C$$

consisting of five terms. The Karnaugh map looks considerably simpler than either the circuit or the expression, as Figure 4.11 shows. The obvious group to go for, Figure 4.12, is the square of 1's that occur in all the lines where A=1, so that this set represents the term A. The less-obvious grouping is of the odd 1 at the top left hand corner with the 1 at the bottom of the same column. This occurs where C=0 and B=0, so that it represents the term:

$$\overline{C} . \overline{B}$$

making the complete expression equal to:

$$Q = A + \overline{C}.\overline{B}$$

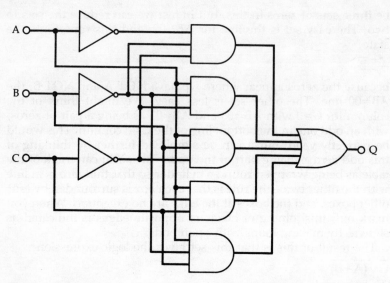

Figure 4.10 A circuit for analysis by Karnaugh mapping. There are five terms OR'd together in the expression

AB	0	1
00	1	0
01	0	0
11	1	1
10	1	1

C

Figure 4.11 The resulting Karnaugh map, showing some obvious groupings and some that are less obvious

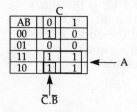

Figure 4.12 Marking the groupings.

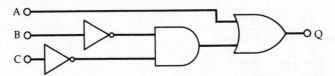

Figure 4.13 The simplified circuit resulting from Karnaugh mapping

and the simplified circuit is as in Figure 4.13, using two gates and two inverters. Later we shall see that the combination of a gate and two inverters can be replaced by one gate, and in this case, the B and C inputs could be into a NOR gate rather than into the inverters and AND gate as shown. This would make the circuit a two-gate one, much simpler than the original.

De Morgan's theorems

George Boole corresponded extensively with another mathematician, De Morgan, who took great interest in Boole's scheme of symbolic logic, and suggested two equivalences that we now know as De Morgan's theorems. We have already met the consequences of these theorems in the form of using NAND and NOR gates to construct AND and OR gating actions. They are of immense value in logic equations, because they allow the easy transformation of equations that use standard gates and inverters into equations that use the NAND/NOR type of gates. This often allows a very awkward-looking gate circuit to be transformed into something quite reasonable, or an expression that consists of a lot of terms ANDed together to be transformed into one that is ORed, so allowing a Karnaugh map to be constructed. De Morgan's theorems, in short, are an essential part of making good use of Boolean algebra.

The first theorem is:

$$\overline{A}.\overline{B} = \overline{(A + B)}$$

meaning that the AND of NOT A and NOT B is identical to A NOR B (meaning NOT A OR B). Figure 4.14 shows the truth tables drawn up that illustrate the identity of these expressions. In gate form, this looks as Figure 4.15, with the combination of two

Gates–further analysis

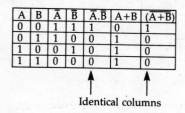

A	B	Ā	B̄	Ā.B̄	A+B	(A+B)
0	0	1	1	1	0	1
0	1	1	0	0	1	0
1	0	0	1	0	1	0
1	1	0	0	0	1	0

Identical columns

Figure 4.14 A truth table to illustrate De Morgan's first theorem

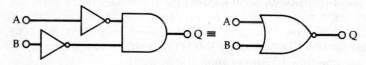

Figure 4.15 The first theorem of De Morgan illustrated in gate form

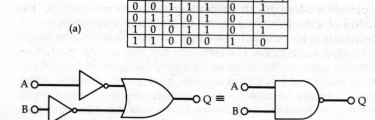

A	B	Ā	B̄	Ā+B̄	A.B	(A.B)
0	0	1	1	1	0	1
0	1	1	0	1	0	1
1	0	0	1	1	0	1
1	1	0	0	0	1	0

(a)

Figure 4.16 (a) De Morgan's second theorem in truth table form and also (b) in gate form

inverters and the AND gate being identical to the NOR gate. The second De Morgan theorem is:

$$\overline{A} + \overline{B} = \overline{(A \cdot B)}$$

which gives the equivalent for the NAND gate. Figure 4.16 shows the truth tables and the equivalent gates.

Armed with the two De Morgan theorems, we can carry out a lot of useful conversions. One such conversion is from AND to OR, so that we can get the action of a gate circuit into the form of a set of ORed terms that can be dealt with by using Karnaugh maps. Another is the more practical point of arranging Boolean equations into forms that allow for gate construction with NAND and NOR gates in place of the use of AND and OR with inverters. These manipulations require considerable practice, however, and until you have seen a few examples worked it is very difficult to see just how useful the De Morgan rules are.

Consider, for example, the impressive looking Boolean equation:

$$Q = (A + B) . (\overline{A} . \overline{B})$$

which would require three gates and two inverters to construct. De Morgan's theorem shows that:

$$\overline{A} . \overline{B} = \overline{(A + B)}$$

so that we can make the substitution to give:

$$Q = (A + B) . \overline{(A + B)}$$

and since we can treat $(A+B)$ as a unit, and since $X.\overline{X} = 0$, then this boils down to $Q=0$. In words, there is no output from this gate for any combination of inputs. You could, of course, show this by using truth tables, but in a very long-winded way. This is an example of De Morgan's theorems being used in *minimisation*, the reduction of a Boolean equation to its simplest possible terms.

Minimisation is not usually as simple as this, and, as in any kind of algebraic manipulation, the more practice you can get the better. There is no space in this book to give as many examples as would illustrate every point about this work, but you can gain as much practice as you need for yourself by devising gate circuits and finding out what they do by using Boolean methods, checking always with the truth tables that your work is correct. Remember that there often is no single simplest Boolean equation, and it is

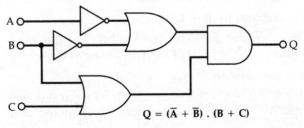

$$Q = (\overline{A} + \overline{B}) . (B + C)$$

Figure 4.17 A circuit example that can be transformed by using De Morgan's theorem

much more common to find that you can get several options, all requiring about the same number of gates.

Now look at another example which starts with the gate equation in Figure 4.17, using two OR gates, two inverters and an AND gate. You can probably tell from from the circuit that the two inverters and the OR gate could be replaced by a NAND gate, but we'll stick with the algebraic route. This starts, as usual, with the equations of the gate circuit:

$$Q = (\bar{A} + \bar{B}) \cdot (B + C)$$

and we can use a De Morgan transformation on the $(\bar{A} + \bar{B})$ term, converting this into A NAND B to make the equation into:

$$\overline{(A.B)} \cdot (B + C)$$

which would be carried out by a combination of a NAND gate, an OR and an AND as illustrated in Figure 4.18.

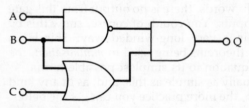

Figure 4.18 The transformed circuit

There is an alternative, which gives a very different-looking result and which takes the use of the De Morgan theorems a step further. This time, we can carry out the conversion of the first term into its NAND form as before, but we can work on the second term also. Since NOT NOT X = X, we can write:

$$\overline{\overline{(B + C)}} \text{ which is identical to } (B + C)$$

Under the top layer of bar, the outer layer of NOT in this term which can be written as NOT(NOT(B OR C)), we have the term

$$\overline{(B + C)} \text{ which is equivalent to } (\bar{B} \cdot \bar{C})$$

which is NOT B and NOT C. This uses the De Morgan theorem for the NOR gate. We still have an outer NOT bar hanging over this lot, so that:

$$\overline{\bar{B} \cdot \bar{C}} \text{ is equivalent to } (B + C) \text{ and this makes the expression into}$$

$$\overline{(A \cdot B)} \cdot \overline{\overline{(B \cdot C)}}$$

This is where you need to take a deep breath. If this looked simple, like

$$\overline{X} \cdot \overline{Y}$$

you would recognise at once that it could be converted, using De Morgan, into

$$\overline{X + Y}$$

so if you think of X as being (A . B) and Y as being $(\overline{B} \cdot \overline{C})$ then you can convert into the form:

$$\overline{(A \cdot B) + (\overline{B} \cdot \overline{C})}$$

which would use three gates and two inverters, or we could re-convert the second term to give:

$$\overline{(A \cdot B) + (\overline{B + C})}$$

which does not look nearly so bad when it is put into gate form, as in Figure 4.19, since it needs only three gates.

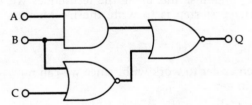

Figure 4.19 An alternative transformation which uses fewer gate *types*

Now that you have fought your way through all this, it's time to take stock. The important point is that there is no unique solution to most logic problems, and if you want to find the solution that is closest to your requirements, you need to state these requirements clearly and work on the equations fairly extensively. It is unusual to find that you get just what you want first time round, and you may have to make use of the De Morgan theorems several times, converting and reconverting as the opportunity presents itself. You don't always see clearly when you can use De Morgan on an equation, particularly when two groups of statements are involved, as this latter example has shown.

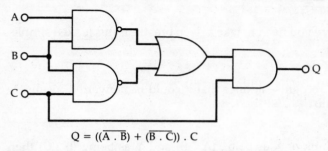

$$Q = ((\overline{A \cdot B}) + (\overline{B \cdot C})) \cdot C$$

Figure 4.20 A circuit for simplification by using De Morgan's theorems

Now look at the example in Figure 4.20, consisting of two NAND gates, one AND gate and one OR gate. In the first stages, we have NOT(A.B) and NOT(B.C), and the outputs of these are ORed. The output of the OR gate is ANDed with C to give the final output Q. In Boolean terms, this is:

$$Q = ((\overline{A \cdot B}) + (\overline{B \cdot C})) \cdot C$$

and we should be able to minimise this using the techniques we have learned to date. The first step is to write the De Morgan equivalents:

$$Q = ((\overline{A} + \overline{B}) + (\overline{B} + \overline{C})) \cdot C$$

which makes the equation easier to work with, since we can now 'multiply out' the terms to get

$$Q = C \cdot \overline{A} + C \cdot \overline{B} + C \cdot \overline{B} + C \cdot \overline{C}$$

and then simplify. The C AND NOT C term goes out entirely, and we don't need to have the C AND NOT B term more than once, leaving:

$$Q = C \cdot \overline{A} + C \cdot \overline{B}$$

which can then be gathered up again as

$$Q = C \cdot (\overline{A} + \overline{B})$$

and then we can use De Morgan again to get

$$Q = C \cdot (\overline{A \cdot B})$$

which makes the circuit one that contains a NAND gate and an AND gate only. This is quite a substantial improvement on the original.

Truth table to gates

It's time now to look at a more extended example which involves starting from a truth table, and applying the principles that we have used so far for finding how the truth table could be implemented. The example consists of more than one truth table, in fact, as Figure 4.21 shows. This is a comparison of the ordinary

	Gray			Binary		
No.	X	Y	Z	A	B	C
0	0	0	0	0	0	0
1	0	0	1	0	0	1
2	0	1	1	0	1	0
3	0	1	0	0	1	1
4	1	1	0	1	0	0
5	1	1	1	1	0	1
6	1	0	1	1	1	0
7	1	0	0	1	1	1

Figure 4.21 A table comparing Gray code and 8-4-2-1 binary

8-4-2-1 binary scale with the Gray code, for three digits only to avoid over-complicating the example. The challenge is to devise a set of gate circuits which will convert Gray code inputs into standard binary code outputs. This means that we need a gate system which has three inputs, X, Y and Z, and three outputs A, B and C. We do *not*, however, need to work with all six quantities at one time.

A look at the truth table shows at once that the digit A, the most significant digit of the binary scale table, is identical to the most significant digit, X, of the Gray code. No conversion is needed for this one, then, greatly simplifying the task. I must emphasise that this is a fortunate coincidence, and if we were converting 4-bit Gray code all the way, we would not find that this remained true for counts above denary 7.

The real work starts when we convert the other digits. This involves writing an expression for the binary digit in terms of the Gray code digits, looking carefully at the truth table. Take, as the next example, the B digit. This is 1 when Y=1 AND X=0 or when Y=0 and X=1, irrespective of the value of Z. We can write this as:

$$B = \bar{X} . Y + X . \bar{Y}$$

and this, as you should remember, is the action of an XOR gate. We can therefore find the second digit by using an XOR gate on the first two digits of the Gray code input.

The last digit is not so simple. From the truth table, we need:

$$C = \bar{X} . \bar{Y}. Z + \bar{X} . Y. \bar{Z} + X . Y . Z + X . \bar{Y} . \bar{Z}$$

taking each line in which C=1 in the usual way. A quick look at a Karnaugh map might be useful to find if this line can be simplified any further, and as Figure 4.22 shows, the result is negative. The

	C	
AB	0	1
00	0	1
01	1	0
11	0	1
10	1	0

Figure 4.22 A Karnaugh map for the C digit of the Grey code in terms of 8-4-2-1 binary

1's in the Karnaugh map are sprinkled around, forming no pattern that we can take advantage of. This does not mean that we cannot make something of the equation, however.

By regrouping, we get to:

$$C = \bar{X}. (\bar{Y}.Z + Y.\bar{Z}) + X. (Y.Z + \bar{Y}.\bar{Z})$$

which, though it does not look particularly clearer, has some practical advantages. The term:

$$\bar{Y}.Z + Y.\bar{Z}$$

for example, is the action of the XOR gate on Y and Z, so that we do not have to make our own arrangements in the form of inverters and a mixture of AND and OR gates in order to to carry this out.

This makes the conversion circuit as shown in Figure 4.23. This is by no means a simple looking circuit, but the use of the XOR gates has in fact simplified the diagram very considerably, as has the simple A to X connection that we can get away with when we convert only three digits. The example is by no means trivial, because the conversion from Gray code to 8-4-2-1 binary is very important, and this emphasises that a logic circuit can be constructed for any such conversion, whatever its nature.

The Karnaugh maps that we have looked at so far have all used only three variables, mainly because this is the minimum number for which the technique is useful and also a reasonable number for simple examples. We can, however, use the Karnaugh map for four variables without too much strain, though this naturally makes the map larger. Figure 4.24 shows the outline of the map,

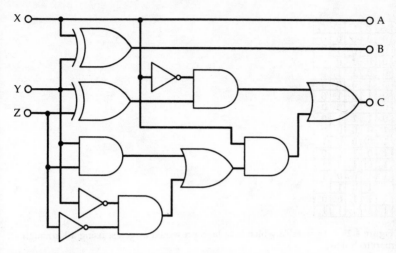

Figure 4.23 The Gray code to binary converter circuit

		CD		
AB	00	01	11	10
00				
01				
11				
10				

Figure 4.24 The outline of a four-input Karnaugh map. Care has to be taken in filling in these maps, because truth tables do not necessarily present the data in the same ABCD order

with the order of digits maintained as 00, 01, 11, 10 as before, but this time for the rows as well as the columns. Each column now represents the variables C and D, each row A and B as before.

An example is shown in Figure 4.25, using a truth table in which the outputs for the combinations of four inputs are as shown. The Q output of the table shows that only five combinations give a 1 output, and we can form a Boolean equation by writing down the conditions for each of these lines. Taken in order down the table, they give

$$Q = A.\bar{B}.\bar{C}.D + A.\bar{B}.C.D + A.B.\bar{C}.\bar{D} + A.B.\bar{C}.D + A.B.C.D$$

and we can now fill in the Karnaugh map with this lot, putting a 1 in the appropriate box for each fulfilled condition, as shown in Figure 4.26. The Karnaugh map shows a block of four 1's which

87

Gates–further analysis

A	B	C	D	Q
0	0	0	0	0
0	0	0	1	0
0	0	1	0	0
0	0	1	1	0
0	1	0	0	0
0	1	0	1	0
0	1	1	0	0
0	1	1	1	0
1	0	0	0	0
1	0	0	0	1
1	0	1	0	0
1	0	1	1	1
1	1	0	0	1
1	1	0	1	1
1	1	1	0	0
1	1	1	1	1

Figure 4.25 A truth table which is to be represented as gates, using a Karnaugh map technique

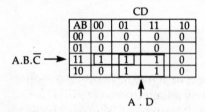

A.B.$\overline{\text{C}}$ →

A . D

Figure 4.26 The completed Karnaugh map, showing groupings

represent the term A.D, and the pair of 1's which is A AND B AND NOT C. The complete expression, then is

$$Q = A.D + A.B.\overline{C}$$

requiring three gates only—you can draw the gate circuit for yourself and check the truth table (which needs 16 lines). This, incidentally, is a case where the Karnaugh map is a very much easier method than trying to resolve the Boolean equation. If you insist on trying, draw up the condition for NOT Q rather than for Q, since this is the one that leads to the same end result.

Comparing numbers

A frequent requirement in logic circuits is to compare two binary numbers, and the usual requirement is to have an output that is 1

88

if one number is greater than or equal to another. This, of course, is available in IC form, but an understanding of the process is useful if you need to make unusual comparisons (comparing two Gray code numbers, for example) and to illustrate that Boolean algebra by itself and at its basic level is not enough to solve a problem.

Suppose, then, that we have two numbers ABC and A'B'C' — we have taken three-bit numbers for simplicity, though a four-bit comparison is generally more useful. Of these numbers, A and A' are the most significant bits, and C and C' the least significant bits; Figure 4.27. The circuit that we shall design will have six inputs,

A	B	C	A'	B'	C'
0	0	0	0	0	0
0	0	1	0	0	1
0	1	0	0	1	0
0	1	1	0	1	1
1	0	0	1	0	0
1	0	1	1	0	1
1	1	0	1	1	0
1	1	1	1	1	1

Table shows equal values for ABC and A'B'C'. A value of A'B'C' is less than that of ABC if it occurs higher in this table.

Figure 4.27 Number comparison table — a preliminary to the design of a 3-bit comparator

A	A'	Q
1	1	1
0	0	1
1	0	0
0	1	0

Q is 1 if A = A'

Figure 4.28 Truth table for equality of A and A'

one for each digit, and an output Q. The output Q shall be 1 if the number ABC is equal to or greater than the number A'B'C', but 0 otherwise.

The conditions for equality are simple enough, and if all you wanted was to establish if two numbers were equal, the gating would appear to be easy. The numbers are equal if A=A' AND B=B' AND C=C' so that three comparisons can be ANDed to give this output. When we look at this more closely, however, we find that we need a truth table to check equality that looks like Figure 4.28, taking only A and A' as an example. This is exactly the inverse of the XOR gate, and is one of the few applications for a

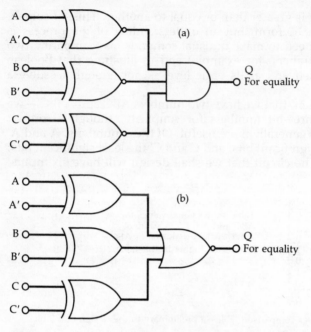

Figure 4.29 Alternative circuits for checking equality using (a) XNOR gates or (b) XOR gates

XNOR gate, of which there is one in the 74 series, the 74266. To check equality, then, we take the digit pairs into XNOR gates and AND the results. As an alternative, we could XOR the digits and NOR the results, and I leave it to you to confirm that these two, Figure 4.29, give equivalent results.

The more difficult part, at first sight, is to give Q=1 when ABC is greater than A'B'C', assuming that equality has been separately tested. As it happens, it is just as easy to make both tests in the same circuit, so that there is no need to OR the results of two separate tests, both of which involve such similar steps. We can dispose of some parts of this problem by looking at the number tables. If A > A', then the number ABC is certainly greater than A'B'C', but this simple relationship does not hold good for the other digits.

We can, however, by looking at the digits, find what the other conditions are. If A=A', then ABC > A'B'C' if B>B'. If A=A' AND B=B', then ABC > A'B'C' only if C>C'. The conditions are

(a) ABC>A'B'C' if:
        A>A'
    OR A=A' AND B>B'
    OR A=A' AND B=B' AND (C>C' OR C=C')
    Note: this last line also tests for complete equality.
(b) Q1 = A.$\bar{A}$'
     Q2 = (A XNOR A').B.$\bar{B}$'
     Q3 = (A XNOR A').(B XNOR B').(C.C' + C XNOR C')

Figure 4.30 Complete Boolean conditions (a) for comparison, including equality. The equations in (b) make use of XNOR rather than the full gate description

therefore as noted in Figure 4.30(a). The problem now is to turn them into Boolean statements, and we can simplify this considerably if we use XNOR to mean the XNOR gate, the gate which gives a 1 output when two inputs are identical. Figure 4.30(b) shows the circuit described in this way, with Q meaning the result of a comparision and this allows us to draw up a gate circuit, as in Figure 4.31. This is the kind of effort for which the established

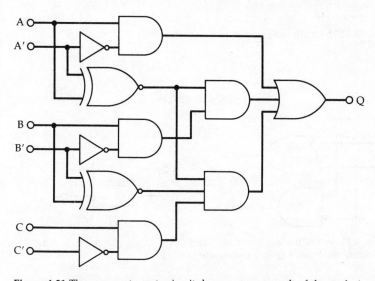

Figure 4.31 The comparator gate circuit drawn up as a result of the analysis

methods of Boolean algebra and Karnaugh maps are least useful because of the number of inputs, six in this example. There is, however, another approach to this type of problem, based on arithmetical circuits.

Arithmetic addition

Arithmetic with a single binary digit is simple and straightforward if that digit happens to be the least significant digit. What we need to do is summarised in the truth table of Figure 4.32, in which the two inputs are A and B, and S is Sum, C is Carry. The table shows that for a 00 input, sum and carry are both zero, a 01 or 10 inputs gives sum 1 and carry 0, and a 11 input gives sum 0 and carry 1. This, then, is a gate circuit with two inputs and two outputs, and we have to form Boolean equations for both outputs. These are simple—the sum is A XOR B and the carry is A AND B, so that the gate circuit is as shown in Figure 4.33. We can even form a symbol for this circuit which, though unofficial, is useful.

A	B	S	C
0	0	0	0
0	1	1	0
1	0	1	0
1	1	0	1

Figure 4.32 The truth table for a binary half-adder

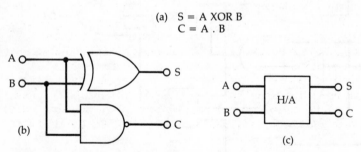

(a) S = A XOR B
     C = A . B

(b)

(c)

Figure 4.33 (a) The Boolean terms for S and C. (b) A gate circuit which will implement the logic, and (c) a convenient symbol

For a number that consists of more than one digit, though, the half-adder is not useful for any but the least significant digits. The reason is that in any other digit addition, there will not be just the two input digits to add but also a carry from the previous stage. If we label this carry C_{in} and the outward carry C_{out}, then the truth

A	B	Cin	S	Cout
0	0	0	0	0
0	0	1	1	0
0	1	0	1	0
0	1	1	0	1
1	0	0	1	0
1	0	1	0	1
1	1	0	0	1
1	1	1	1	1

Figure 4.34 The truth table for a full adder, which includes a carry bit in as well as a carry bit out

table for a full adder looks as in Figure 4.34. The first part of this truth table is just that of a half-adder with inputs B and C_{in}, but if you become mesmerised by this point, the solution of the rest of the problem becomes more difficult. The easiest way to look at the problem is from the viewpoint of a half-adder. We can half-add the inputs A and B, and get a sum or a carry bit out. The sum is then added to the carry in, since we want to add A + B + C_{in}, and adding the sum to C_{in} does this action. Now if there is a carry from A + B, there cannot be a carry from C_{in} + (A+B), because when there is a carry from the half-adder, there is no sum. The carry can be from one half-adder or the other, never both, so that these carry bits can be ORed to give the final carry.

This can be represented by the gate diagram shown in Figure 4.35, using the two half-adders and the OR gate to give the required output, as you can check by drawing up a truth table showing all of the quantities. The weakness of traditional Boolean algebra is that it has not been extended to provide symbols for the units that we can make in IC form. Boolean algebra can provide an analysis of this circuit in terms of AND, OR and NOT gates, but that would be to turn our back on very useful ICs that exist and which should be used. The same is true of XOR and XNOR

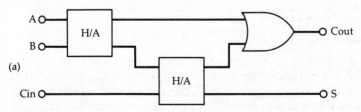

Figure 4.35 The circuit for a full adder in terms of half-adders

gates, both of which can be very useful though not provided for in Boolean algebra except in their fundamental forms.

Subtraction

Subtraction can be carried out in digital logic in two ways. One is to form the complement of one number and then add, the other is to perform the subtraction, using subtracter circuits that are designed in the same way as adder circuits. The difference is that in place of a carry we have a borrow, a bit that will be subtracted from the next higher digits rather than added to them. If we imagine that digit B is to be subtracted from digit A, then a half-subtracter (the least significant digits) will have a truth table as in Figure 4.36. The table for the result S is identical to that for the half-adder, and can be carried out by an XOR gate as before. The table for the borrow has a 1 corresponding to B AND NOT A, and can be carried out using an inverter and an AND gate, as indicated in Figure 4.37.

Now suppose we need to subtract two digits when there may be a borrow to subtract as well? The truth table for such a full

A – B		$\overline{C}$	S
0	0	0	0
0	1	1	1
1	0	0	1
1	1	0	0

Note: C means borrow, the opposite of carry.

Figure 4.36 A truth table for a half-subtracter

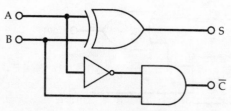

Figure 4.37 A circuit that performs the half-subtraction action

A	−	B	−	$\overline{C}$in	S	$\overline{C}$out
0		0		0	0	0
0		0		1	1	1
0		1		0	1·	1
0		1		1	0	1
1		0		0	1	0
1		0		1	0	0
1		1		0	0	0
1		1		1	1	1

Figure 4.38 The truth table for a full subtracter, with a borrow in as well as a borrow out

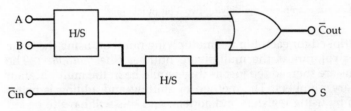

Figure 4.39 The gate circuit for the full subtracter. These subtracter circuits are not available in IC form, because it is usually more convenient to work by adding a negative number

subtracter is shown in Figure 4.38. As you might expect, the table for the S output is identical to that of the full adder, and only the borrow output is different. On the basis of the similarity between the half-subtracter and the half-adder, we might expect that the circuit of Figure 4.39 would provide for full subtraction, and it does, providing that we remember that the symbol in the box means that this is a half-subtracter. Neither half nor full subtracters are made in IC form in the 74 series, because of the almost universal use of complementary addition in place of subtraction, so that for special purposes the circuit shown here might be useful.

Subtraction is another way of comparing numbers, because if we have, for example, a three-bit subtraction circuit (two full subtracters and a half-subtracter) then one number is greater than the other if the final carry bit is 1, and the two are equal if all the output bits are 0. This can, for numbers of several digits, be an easier method than the use of comparators, and if a complementary addition is used, the ICs are readily available.

Multiplication

Binary multiplication follows the rules that you might expect, that $0 \times 0 = 0$, 1×0 or $0 \times 1 = 0$ and $1 \times 1 = 1$. Figure 4.40 illustrates the multiplication of two three-bit numbers, from which you can see that the process involves writing down the number that is to

```
    101
×   011
    101    Least significant digit
    101
    000    Most significant digit
  01111
```

Figure 4.40 An example of multiplying two 3-bit numbers

be multiplied for each 1 in the multiplying number, using the same starting column as the multiplying number (the *multiplier*). The columns are then added just as they would be in the multiplication of denary numbers. The method of shifting and adding is better tackled by using registers and adders, and this will have to be left for later, but it is possible to treat multiplication as a logic process, with inputs and outputs.

Suppose, for example that we have to multiply two 2-digit numbers together. The result of such a multiplication can be a number with up to four digits, because $11 \times 11 = 1001$, the largest possible result. We can draw up a table with all the possible sets of two-digit numbers and their results, labelling the inputs as AB and CD, and the output as WXYZ. This table is in Figure 4.41, and

A	B	C	D	W	X	Y	Z
0	0	any		0	0	0	0
any		0	0	0	0	0	0
0	1	0	1	0	0	0	1
1	0	0	1	0	0	1	0
0	1	1	0	0	0	1	0
1	0	1	0	0	1	0	0
0	1	1	1	0	0	1	1
1	0	1	1	0	1	1	0
1	1	1	1	1	0	0	1
1	1	0	1	0	0	1	1
1	1	1	0	0	1	1	0

Figure 4.41 A truth table for the multiplication of all possible 3-bit numbers, allowing the action to be carried out by gates. Note later that shift-and-add techniques can also be used, but these require more time

you can see that we could have excluded for a start all the lines in which AB=00 or CD=00. From this table, we can draw up the logical lines for each of the outputs W, X, Y and Z, of which W is the simplest. From the table you can see that W=1 only for the condition A.B.C.D so that we can write down this condition at once. The derivation of Z is equally easy, because this occurs only for B.D, and we can write this one down also. The more tricky ones are for X and Y.

Of these, X is the easier, because it occurs in only three lines. This shows that the conditions for X are:

$$A.\bar{B}.C.\bar{D} + A.\bar{B}.C.D. + A.B.C.\bar{D}$$

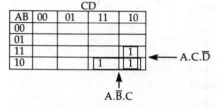

Figure 4.42 A Karnaugh map for quantity X, showing only the 1 boxes

and when we draw up a Karnaugh map for this, Figure 4.42, we find that we can reduce this to

$$A.\bar{B}.C + A.C.\bar{D}$$

The equation for Y is more complicated, because there is a 1 for Y in six of the lines of the truth table. Figure 4.43 shows these lines in the form of a truth table, and then the Karnaugh map formed from them. This can be simplified into:

$$Y = A.D.(\bar{B} + \bar{C}) + \bar{A} . \bar{D} . (B + C)$$

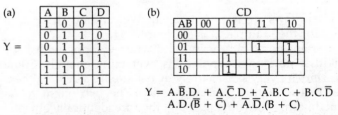

Figure 4.43 The truth table (a) for the quantity Y and the resulting Karnaugh map (b) and expression

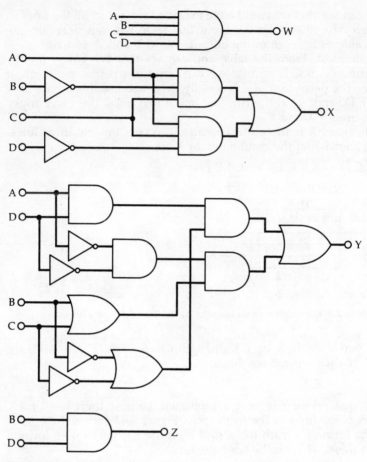

Figure 4.44 The complete gate circuit for the multiplier

so that all four laws are now completed. We can now draw up a gate circuit for the multiplier, as in Figure 4.44.

The important point to bear in mind when working with logic circuits is that no single approach is ever quite enough. Some equations simplify very satisfactorily by using pure algebra, others are better treated with a Karnaugh map. The two ought to be equivalent, but this does not mean that they are identically obvious and easy, and you have to switch between the two, looking for simplifications. Working with a large number of inputs and outputs can become very tedious, and if you can make 'short-circuits' by using such devices as XOR gates and adders which exist in IC form though not in simple Boolean terms, then you can proceed faster. The main problem is that a given equation can often be simplified to several different, though equivalent, forms, and it is up to the designer to decide which form to use. This implies that you ought not to be satisfied with one form, because there could be another one lurking somewhere that might be easier to construct.

5 Sequential action

Gate circuits are combinational, meaning that the output at any given time depends entirely on the state of the inputs at that time. The delay time between altering an input and having the output alter correspondingly (when such an alteration is specified by the truth table) is very short, of the order of nanoseconds for all but the slowest types of ICs. As we have seen, gate circuits are versatile and can perform logic actions which include the actions of arithmetic, comparison, code translation and others. In addition, gate circuits are fundamental circuits in the sense that all of the devices used in digital circuitry could be constructed from gates, though the internal circuitry of ICs need not necessarily take such a form.

The use of cross-coupled feedback between inverting gates (NAND or NOR) makes possible the construction of circuit elements called flip-flops whose characteristics are very different from those of the gate circuits that we have looked at so far. The traditional type of cross-coupled transistor circuit is typified by the astable multivibrator of Figure 5.1, which generates steep-sided waveforms that approximate to a square wave at each collector. The simple transistor multivibrator circuit requires considerable modification if it is to produce waveforms with really steep sides whose switching times are short enough to compare with digital circuits, and the flip-flop circuits that are used for digital work are very seldom astable (oscillating continually). The usual requirement is for a bistable circuit, in which an output will remain at either 0 or 1 until an input changes the state of the circuit.

Figure 5.2 shows a cross-coupled circuit using NAND gates as the active devices. The coupling is direct, since the output of a gate can be coupled directly to the input of any other gate, with the inputs labelled as R and S and output Q and NOT Q. For a circuit

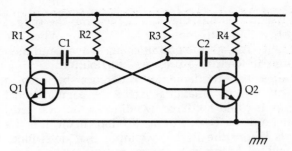

Figure 5.1 The traditional astable multivibrator circuit, using two bipolar transistors. The output is taken from one collector, and though a good fall-time can be achieved, the rise time is poor because stray capacitances have to be charged through the collector load resistor

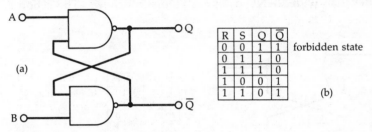

R	S	Q	$\overline{Q}$	
0	0	1	1	forbidden state
0	1	1	0	
1	1	1	0	
1	0	0	1	
1	1	0	1	(b)

Figure 5.2 One form of flip-flop using NAND gates (a) and the resulting state table (b) showing the store state of R=1; S=1

like this, the table that we can draw up is not so much a truth table in the sense that we use this name for other gate circuits, but a *state table* which shows what changes in the outputs are achieved for changes in the inputs. The circuit action can be followed by reference to the truth table for a NAND gate.

In the first line, a 0 at the R input will force Q to be 1, and the 0 input to S will force NOT Q to be 1 also. This is therefore a false or forbidden state, since the labelling of the outputs as Q and NOT Q suggests that one ought always to be the inverse of the other. When this type of flip-flop is used, then, the state of R=0, S=0 is avoided (by using gating, for example) so as not to have this output unless it is required for special purposes.

The R=0, S=1 state in the second line gives the Q=1 output, because R=0 forces Q=1, and the 1 AND 1 input to the second gate forces the NOT Q output to 0. At this point, the state table departs from the usual routine of a truth table, because the next state is R=1, S=1, and this has the effect of leaving the output unchanged at Q=1, with a corresponding NOT Q (=0). When the input is changed to R=1, S=0, the output changes over, and then a subsequent change to R=1, S=1 preserves this output.

This demonstrates the fundamental difference between a sequential circuit and a combinational circuit. A combinational circuit with two inputs could not have two different output states for the same inputs of R=1, S=1. In this flip-flop circuit, it is the sequence of inputs before the R=1, S=1 input that determines what the output will be. In this case, the output is determined by either R=0, S=1 or R=1, S=0, and the R=1, S=1 state simply retains the previous state. The R=1, S=1 state is therefore called the 'store' or 'lock' state of the flip-flop.

Another form of RS flip-flop can be constructed with NOR gates rather than with NAND gates, as Figure 5.3 shows. The action is

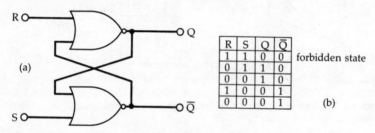

R	S	Q	$\overline{Q}$	
1	1	0	0	forbidden state
0	1	1	0	
0	0	1	0	
1	0	0	1	
0	0	0	1	(b)

Figure 5.3 The flip-flop constructed from NOR gates (a) and the state table (b) which now requires R=0; S=0 for storing

similar, but not identical because for this circuit the R=1, S=1 state is the forbidden state, in which the Q and NOT Q outputs are both 0, and the locking state is R=0, S=0

The RS flip-flop in any form has few applications, so that it is not available in IC form, but has to be made up from NAND or NOR gates as needed. The few applications it has, however, are often useful. One such application is to the *debouncing* of switches. When a mechanical switch is closed the elasticity of the metal arms that carry the contacts leads to the contacts coming together and then bouncing open again, and this bouncing may be repeated several times before the switch finally closes. If the switch is being used to generate a pulse, then the bouncing action will cause several pulses to be generated each time the switch is closed, and

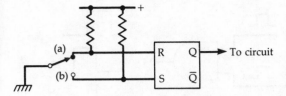

Figure 5.4 Debouncing a mechanical switch by using the R-S flip-flop

this can lead to incorrect operation of the equipment for which the switch provides an input.

Debouncing is provided by the circuit of Figure 5.4. When the switch is in position (a), the R terminal is earthed, so that the input state is R=0, S=1 because of the pull-up resistor connected to the S input. For the NAND gate type of RS flip-flop, this will give Q=1 as the output. Now when the switch is changed over, the contact will momentarily be between R and S, so that R=1, S=1, retaining the output at Q=1. When the moving contact of the switch reaches position (b), it will earth the S input, changing the output over to Q=0. If the contact now bounces, leaving the S-connection open, the effect of the pull-up resistor will be to make R=1, S=1, retaining the Q=0 output while the switch bounces. The bouncing will therefore have no effect unless it is so severe that the contact bounces back to position (a) again, which is most unlikely. Each switchover is therefore electrically 'clean', generating a square-sided single transition from 0 to 1 or 1 to 0. Every mechanical switch that is used to provide a signal input to a digital circuit should be debounced in this way.

Triggered flip-flop

The RS flip-flop responds to a change at the two inputs, and each of its two stable states is achieved by setting one input (to 1) and resetting (to 0) the other. In this respect, the RS flip-flop behaves rather like other circuits constructed from gates in that its output will change whenever these input changes take place. The usefulness of the RS flip-flop is decidedly limited by this to applications, such as switch debouncing, in which the storage that occurs for R=1, S=1 is important.

The circuits that make use of flip-flops, however, are generally controlled by a clock pulse, a pulse that exists on a line at regular

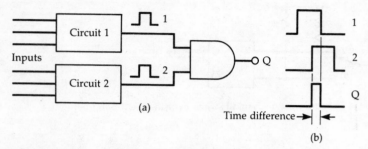

Figure 5.5 Race hazards—the output in this example depends on the time of overlap of two pulses, and an excessive delay in one pulse could result in no output appearing, since the 1 states are not stored

intervals and which controls the timing of the circuit. Timing with a clock pulse allows actions to be carried out in sequence, and it also avoids a problem that can occur in large gate circuits, the *race hazard*. To see what is involved in a race hazard, imagine that two gate circuits feed an AND gate, Figure 5.5(a). The feeder circuits will have various inputs and each will deliver a brief pulse to the inputs of the AND gate. The output of this gate will therefore be a brief pulse whose duration will be the common duration of the two inputs, Figure 5.5(b).

Now suppose that one of the gate circuits involves a much greater number of gates than the other, so that the time between receiving the inputs and delivering the output is greater than that for the other gate. If the duration of each pulse is short, there is a possibility that the pulses could never overlap, so that there would never be an output from the AND gate. It is equally possible to imagine circuits in which brief unwanted pulses could be generated because a gate input changes rather more slowly than another input. When the outputs of gates control slow-acting devices, this is not a problem to worry about, but if the output of the gate circuit is taken to a pulse counter, or to any kind of flip-flop which can change state on receipt of a pulse and then maintain that changed state, then these race hazards are a very serious problem.

The answer is that synchronisation is used, in the form of clock pulses along with storage. The inputs to a device are allowed to change, with no effect on the device until a clock pulse is also present. A change can then only take place at the time of the clock pulse, and in the duration of the clock pulse. Any changes that occur after the end of the clock pulse are similarly ignored.

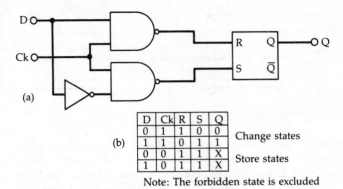

D	Ck	R	S	Q
0	1	1	0	0
1	1	0	1	1
0	0	1	1	X
1	0	1	1	X

(b)   Change states

Store states

Note: The forbidden state is excluded

Figure 5.6 A modified RS flip-flop circuit (a) that allows the use of a clock pulse, with the resulting truth table that also shows the states (b)

Provided that the time between clock pulses is larger than the greatest possible delay in the circuit, and that inputs are stored between clock pulses, there is no possibility of false outputs being generated because of race hazards.

Figure 5.6(a) shows an adaptation to the RS flip-flop that allows it to be used with a clock pulse. The gate circuit that has been added to the basic RS flip-flop consists of two NAND gates, with the clock pulse Ck being taken to one input of each. The input, labelled as D for data, is taken to the gate whose output controls the R input of the flip-flop, and the other input is provided through an inverter. This gives the truth table shown in (b), in which a change at Q is established when the D input changes and the clock input is at logic 1. For a clock input level of 0, the RS flip-flop is always in its store state, irrespective of the level of the D input. Since a store state is a feature of any flip-flop, we can concentrate on the conditions that make a change at the output, and this leads to the state table, which shows the state of the output before the clock pulse (Q−) and the state following the clock pulse (Q+) for each state of the single input D. This simple state table shows that the Q output takes the same level as the D input when the circuit is clocked. These outputs are also often shown as Qt-1 and Qt to indicate before-clocking and after-clocking.

A flip-flop of this type can be regarded as a circuit in its own right, the D-type flip-flop, and given the symbol shown in Figure 5.7(a). A circuit like this is often referred to as a *latch*, and it can fulfil an important action of data capture. Suppose, for example,

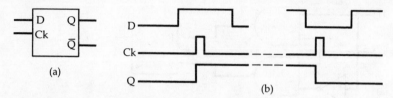

Figure 5.7 The D-type flip-flop symbol (a) and action (b)

that you have a requirement to open a valve in a water pipe, using an electric motor, when a brief pulse arrives at an input. A brief pulse cannot have any effect on an electric motor, but if the brief pulse overlaps a clock pulse, Figure 5.7(b) then the pulse can change over the state of the Q output, and this changed output can activate a relay that operates a motor. The important point is that a brief and transient input can cause an output change which will persist until there is another clocked change at the input. This allows data to be held for at least the time between clock pulses, changing only when the input changes and a clock pulse arrives.

Useful though the latch can be, there is still a problem associated with it. One form of this problem is the race hazard all over again, as illustrated in Figure 5.8(a). The clock pulse in this example has been delayed relative to the data, so that the data changed from 1 to 0 in the time of the clock pulse. This inevitably means that the output of the flip-flop will also make the change from 1 to 0, since the output follows the input for the duration of the clock pulse. The other aspect to this problem is that we can make useful flip-flop circuits which change over each time a clock pulse is received. This involves a feedback link from the NOT Q output to the D inputs, as shown in (b). Using the type of D-type flip-flop we have

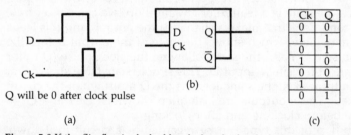

Q will be 0 after clock pulse

(a)

Ck	Q
0	0
1	1
0	1
1	0
0	0
1	1
0	1

(c)

Figure 5.8 If the flip-flop is clocked by clock pulse level, then a change at D during the time of the clock pulse (a) will cause an output change. The feedback circuit (b) is possible only when triggering is by the leading edge of the clock pulse, and (c) shows the resulting state table, a toggling action

described, however, this is an impossible connection. When the NOT Q output is at 0, then it will force D to 0, making Q=0 and NOT Q=1, which will force D to 1, making Q=1 and NOT Q= 0 and so on. It is impossible to predict what the state of the output will be at the end of the clock pulse.

The D-type flip-flop is therefore made in a different form, the edge-triggered D-type. You could imagine that the clock pulse is taken through a capacitive input and differentiated, with only the leading edge spike fed as an input to the gates. This allows the clocking action to exist only for the rise-time of the clock pulse, which is normally considerably less than the time needed for the flip-flop to change over. The edge effect is, in fact, obtained by more elaborate methods, but this is irrelevant to the action. An edge-clocked D-type flip-flop is therefore less likely to be affected by pulse delays, provided that the leading edge of the clock pulse occurs at some stage within the duration of the data pulse input. In addition, the circuit that uses feedback from the NOT Q output back to the D-input becomes possible.

When the Q output goes low in such a circuit, the NOT Q output is high, and this takes the D-input high, but not during the time of the leading edge of the clock pulse. The D-input can then remain high with the Q output low until the leading edge of the next clock pulse. This allows the change over to start, but by the time the NOT Q output has changed over, the D-input no longer has any effect on the output because the delay between triggering the change and completing the change has been greater than the duration of the leading edge of the clock-pulse. Figure 5.8(c) shows the sequence of outputs that can be obtained from an edge-triggered D-type connected in this way.

This table is of a binary count, with two complete cycles of change from 0 to 1 and back being needed in order to carry out one complete cycle of such a change at the output. The input pulses, though labelled as clock pulses, need not be regular provided that they meet the requirements of a very short leading edge. A circuit of this type is described as a *toggling* circuit, and forms the basis of a complete class of counters, the asychronous counters, of which there is much more in the following chapter.

The JK flip-flop

Since the D-type flip-flop can exist in two forms, one level-triggered in the sense that the Q output follows the state of the D input for as long as the clock input is high, and the other edge triggered (with the possibility of either leading or trailing edge being used), the appearance of a D-type in a circuit diagram is no guarantee that the correct form of D-type will be selected. In any case, though the D-type is a well-established form and is reliable, there is something unsatisfactory about using a device that depends so critically on the maintenance of a very sharp leading edge to the clock pulse. It's like relying for playing records on the contact with a diamond stylus which will inevitably alter the shape of the record groove. Like the vinyl disc recording, however, the D-type flip-flop has been useful in the past and is still available as a unit in the 74 series, and as part of other circuits in IC form.

The increasing demands for digital circuitry in the 1960s, however, produced a very different type of flip-flop circuit, one of considerable versatility and which did not rely on the rise time of a clock pulse for its operation. This flip-flop embodies two separate design improvements, and its full name is the JK master-slave flip-flop, which we always abbreviate, not surprisingly, to JK. The master-slave part of the name describes a principle which is very important both for race hazards and for feedback. The form of this flip-flop is as two separate flip-flops, one of which is triggered by the leading edge or the level of a clock pulse, and the other by the trailing edge. Data is read from the inputs at the leading edge of the clock pulse, retained internally, and transferred so as to change the outputs only at the trailing edge of the clock pulse. The rise and fall times of the clock pulse must be maintained reasonably short (short compared to the duration of the clock pulse), but not to the extent that is necessary for the operation of an edge-triggered D-type. The time interval between accepting data in and changing the outputs can then be governed wholly by the duration of the clock pulse, the time between leading edge and trailing edge, something that is not possible with earlier designs.

At the same time, the control of the flip-flop action is improved by using two data inputs, labelled J and K, as well as the clock pulse. These inputs are termed the synchronous inputs, because their action is synchronised to the clock pulse. There are also two other inputs, labelled as asynchronous. Some manufacturers refer to these inputs as 'set' and 'reset', others refer to them as 'preset' and 'clear', and their action is to make the Q output 1 or 0, depending on which input is used, and irrespective of the condition of the clock pulse. These asynchronous inputs are normally maintained at level 1 by a pull-up resistor, and the action of each input is carried out by pulsing the input momentarily to

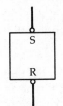

Figure 5.9 The form of symbol used to indicate inputs that require a 0 rather than a 1 for their action

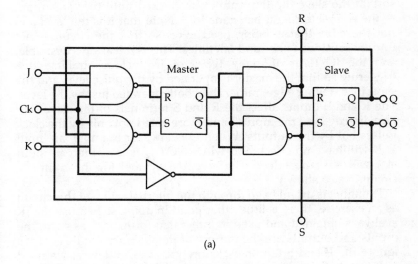

(a)

Note: $\bar{S}$ and $\bar{R}$ used instead of circle symbol to indicate that the action requires a level 0 input.

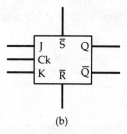

(b)

Figure 5.10 (a) A circuit for one form of JK flip-flop. IC types cannot necessarily be represented accurately by such a circuit, because of interactions within the chip. (b) The JK flip-flop symbol

level 0. This can be indicated in diagrams by showing the input with a small circle, as in Figure 5.9, following the convention that is used to distinguish the NAND gate from the AND gate, and NOR from OR or inverter from buffer.

We seldom need to worry about the internal circuit of a JK, and in integrated form the circuit diagram can be misleading, but as an indication of what is involved, Figure 5.10 shows an equivalent circuit. This contains two RS flip-flops, a master and a slave, each with NAND gates. The clock pulse is taken directly to the first pair of NAND gates, and in inverted form to the second pair of gates so that the slave flip-flop cannot be clocked until the clock input to the complete circuit has gone low. Note that it is the level and not the edge that is being used here, so that the circuit is not unduly sensitive to rise and fall times. This is not always desirable, and the IC form of many types of JK includes trailing-edge triggering so that the master is operated by the pulse level and the slave by a trailing edge, rather than both operated just by the level. The R and S inputs affect the R and S terminals of the slave flip-flop directly, and the inputs J and K are gated not only by the clock pulses but by the outputs. When Q is low, for example, an input at K will have no effect, and when NOT Q is low, then an input at J will have no effect. The accepted symbol for the complete circuit is also shown.

Though it is useful to go through the internal action of this circuit as an exercise, there is little other point in doing so because the JK is always obtained and used in integrated form, and, as such, the inputs and outputs are the important items. Since the JK is, if we ignore the R and S terminals, entirely a clocked device, we need to know the state of the output before and after the clock pulse for each possible combination of inputs at J and K. Several implementations of the JK have no separate S terminal, using only the R terminal to reset the IC so that Q=0. To show the synchronous (clocked) actions, we need to use a state table, as in Figure 5.11,

J	K	Q−	Q+	
0	0	0	0	No change, latch state
0	0	1	1	
0	1	0	0	Reset on clock
0	1	1	0	
1	0	0	1	Set on clock
1	0	1	1	
1	1	0	1	Toggle on clock trailing edge
1	1	1	0	

Figure 5.11 The state table for the JK flip-flop, ignoring the R and S inputs. Q− is used to mean before the clock pulse, and Q+ to mean after the clock pulse

which shows the output following the clock (Q+) for each possible state of previous output (Q−) and inputs at J and K.

This table can be arranged into four sections. With J=0, K=0, the JK is in a store state, and the output after the clock pulse will always be identical to the output before the clock pulse. With J=0, K=1, the output will reset so that Q=0 irrespective of whatever state it was in before the clock pulse. With J=1, K=0 the output will set so that Q=1 irrespective of the state it was in before the clock pulse. Finally, with J=1, K=1, the output will toggle, switching from 0 to 1 or 1 to 0 for each clock pulse. The asynchronous inputs, not shown in this table, allow the output to be set or reset irrespective of the state of the clock.

The advantages of using this form of flip-flop are:

1. It can carry out the action of any previous type of flip-flop.
2. It has no indeterminate states when used synchronously.
3. It need not be critically dependent on clock rise/fall times.
4. The delay time from input to output is short, but the action does not depend on this being short.

These points deserve more consideration. By ignoring the other inputs and using the R and S inputs, the JK can operate independently of the clock, like an unclocked RS. If a single input is applied to the J terminal with an inverter connection to K, the action is that of the D-type. With J=1, K=1, the action is of an edge-triggered D-type with feedback, providing toggling. Any action that would normally be provided by another type of flip-flop can therefore be carried out by the JK type, and since it is as easy to make the JK in IC form, once production has been set up, as to make any other type, this is the preferred type of flip-flop for circuit design.

The lack of indeterminate states is important. The RS design can permit a state in which both Q and NOT Q are at the same logic level. Though this would be possible if the asynchronous inputs of the JK followed the simple pattern shown in Figure 5.10, IC forms of the JK can incorporate gates that prevent this state from being used. The older designs will, however, permit both R and S to be taken low together so that both Q and NOT Q are high, and the output can then be indeterminate if both R and S are changed to level 1 together. The J and K inputs are totally free of such indeterminate effects, however, so that each J and K input state there is an unambiguous action with no possibility of unplanned outputs. The flip-flop *can* make use of clock levels rather than edges, so making operation possible with clock pulses that have

111

quite slow rise and fall times. In the 74 series, it is common to find that the standard 74 ICs allow clock level operation and the LS types use edge triggered action. The difference is important, because when level triggering is used, the J and K inputs must not change while the clock level is high, and edge triggering is necessary to achieve more predictable results.

When edge triggering is used for both input and output, the time between accepting inputs and changing output is the duration of the clock pulse, and this time can be such that it ensures no race hazards by being longer than the longest race delay in the circuit. This implies that there will always be a limit to the speed at which a circuit can be clocked, and that this speed will always be lower than any limit imposed by the response of the flip-flops themselves. It is much more common to find that only the trailing edge is effective, however, so that changes in J and K will have an effect for as long as the clock level is high, but that the change at the output is effective only at the trailing edge of the clock. This makes the response of the flip-flop much faster than it would be if edge triggering were used on both edges, while still preserving the isolation between inputs and outputs.

Other flip-flop types

The JK is the predominant flip-flop type for use in counters and similar circuits, and is available in IC form in a bewildering variety of type numbers and packages. It does not, however, fulfil every possible action that we might require of a cross-coupled device because its coupling is purely DC. It can offer latching and toggling action, in other words, but not oscillation or pulse-timing, and for these actions we need astable and bistable flip-flops respectively.

As it happens, a simple inverter or NAND/NOR gate type can provide the action of an astable flip-flop oscillator. A typical circuit is shown in Figure 5.12, using an inverter, and ignoring the power

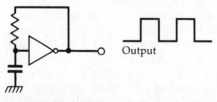

Figure 5.12 An elementary inverter oscillator, making use of the difference between the input voltage levels for *on* and *off*

supply connections as is usual in digital circuits. At switch-on, C will be uncharged so that the input will be at 0, so that when power is applied the output level will rise to 1. This now allows C to charge through R until the input level reaches the point at which the output changes over. The capacitor now discharges through the resistor until the output is forced to change over again. This circuit can operate only if the value of R is low enough to allow the input of the gate to be pulled low, and for standard TTL this requires values in the order of 100–470 ohms. Other types of logic construction which do not have a high current requirement for a low input level can make use of considerably higher values, so that this type of oscillator is more easily constructed from MOS types than from bipolar ones.

The simple inverter type of astable also suffers from having rather indeterminate switching points. Both gates and inverters are designed so as to give unambiguous outputs for equally unambiguous inputs, and there is no guarantee of what can happen when the input level lies between the guaranteed 0 and 1 levels. A much more positive switching action is achieved by the use of a Schmitt trigger gate or inverter, distinguished in a circuit diagram by the symbols shown in Figure 5.13. The basic Schmitt trigger circuit constructed from transistors is shown in Figure 5.14. If we imagine the input held at zero so that the transistor Q1 is non-conducting, the transistor Q2 is held conducting by the resistors connected to the base. The common emitter connections will be at some voltage and for the sake of explanation we can imagine that this is 2V. Now increasing the input voltage will not have any effect on Q1 until the base voltage reaches a level sufficient for conduction, about 2.55V in this example. At this level, Q1 starts to conduct, sending the voltage at the base of Q2 low. This will have the effect of lowering the emitter voltages, making the switchover very fast. With Q1 conducting, lowering the voltage on the base will reduce the emitter voltages, but Q2 will not start to conduct again until the voltage between its base and its emitter has risen to about 0.55V, which may be only after the emitter voltage has reached close to zero.

The characteristics of a circuit like this are illustrated in Figure 5.15. As the input voltage is increased, following the line AC, the output remains at zero until the input voltage reaches C, when the output switches high. Further increases in input level along DE now have no effect. Lowering the input voltage also has no effect while the voltage is on the DF range, but when the input level reaches that of point F, the circuit switches over again, and the

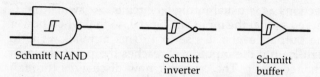

Schmitt NAND   Schmitt   Schmitt
                  inverter   buffer

Figure 5.13 Symbols for Schmitt trigger gates. The inverting types are much more suitable for use in oscillator circuits that the corresponding non-Schmitt types, and the non-inverting buffer can be used to 'clean up' pulses

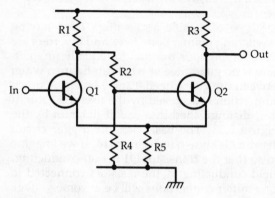

Figure 5.14 The Schmitt trigger in its simplest transistor form

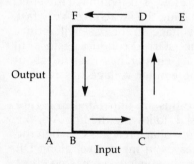

Figure 5.15 The Schmitt trigger action. The output will be either high or low, with no intermediate stage, and the trigger points are C (0 to 1 change) and B (1 to 0 change)

output drops again to zero. The difference between the switching points is represented in this diagram by the lengths BC or DF, and the important feature of the circuit is that the two switchover voltages are different and clearly defined. This is not the case for an inverter, whether conventional or TTL, and it makes the Schmitt circuit very insensitive to small variations in input voltage, ensuring the electrical equivalent of a debounced switch action. The use of one of the Schmitt gates or inverters for an oscillator therefore ensures much more consistent action and a more stable waveform.

The use of Schmitt stages is also a very convenient way of 'cleaning up' a pulse waveform that may have suffered from the effects of stray capacitances or been produced by a circuit which did not allow fast rise or fall times. This can be extended to crystal-controlled oscillators, as shown in Figure 5.16, where the inverter

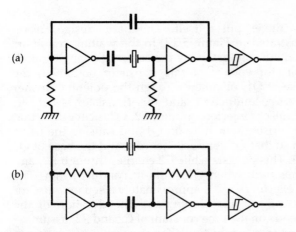

Figure 5.16 Two circuits for crystal-controlled oscillators using Schmitt trigger inverters

oscillator produces a wave of roughly square shape, and the Schmitt inverter, acting also as a buffer, ensures really sharp leading and trailing edges.

The monostable

The purpose of a monostable is to provide a single square pulse output for each brief trigger pulse at the input, irrespective of the

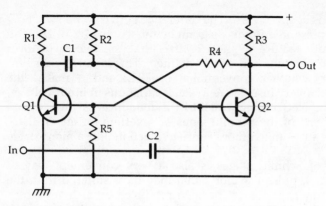

Figure 5.17 The monostable circuit in its simplest transistor form. This allows a pulse of time determined by C1, R2 to be generated from a brief input trigger

duration of the trigger pulse itself. The basic design, using transistors, is illustrated in Figure 5.17. In the waiting condition, transistor Q2 is held in conduction by the current flowing through R2. With the collector voltage of this transistor bottomed, the voltage at the base of Q1, obtained through the potential divider R5/R4, is too low for conduction, and this transistor is cut off. When a negative pulse is injected through C2, Q2 is cut off, so that its collector voltage rises, switching on Q1 and causing the usual switchover action so that Q1 conducts heavily, and the base of Q2 is forced negative. This persists while C2 charges through R2, and the circuit switches back when Q2 starts to conduct again. The output from the collector of Q2 is approximately a square pulse for a negative-going trigger pulse input, and the duration of the output pulse depends on the time constant of C2 and R2, assuming that there is no reverse conduction (Zener conduction) between the base and emitter of Q2.

The circuit in this simple form constructed from discrete components does not generate a particularly well-shaped pulse, and rather than use a more elaborate discrete circuit or to adapt it to digital inverters, it is better to make use of a purpose-made IC for monostable use. ICs like the 74121 are available for this purpose, and have the advantages of good stability of pulse width and several triggering inputs, including two inputs that make use of a Schmitt circuit so that slowly-changing voltages can be used to generate the pulse. There is an internal timing resistor so that variation of pulse width can be achieved by adding an external timing capacitor, with the option of using both an external capacitor and an external resistor, and the circuit is almost unaffected by fluctuations in temperature or supply voltage, subject to the normal TTL limits. An external timing resistor may be added, so that a huge pulse time range of 35 ns to about 28 s can be achieved. The permitted range of external timing resistor is 1K4 to 40K, and the range of external timing capacitors is from 0 to 1000 pF for high stability pulses, up to 1 μF if the trailing edge of the pulse need not have a fast fall time. The pulse shape can, of course, be further trimmed by using a Schmitt trigger on the output.

6 Using flip-flops

Asynchronous counting

An asynchronous counter is one in which each flip-flop is clocked at a different rate, and this implies a counter of the form often called a *ripple* or *ripple-through* counter. The basic form of such a counter, using four JK flip-flops, is shown in Figure 6.1. Each JK is connected in its toggle mode, with both J and K inputs taken to logic 1. The reset inputs are connected together and to a pull-up resistor, with a switch connection (usually a push-to-make switch) to earth. The pulse input is to the clock input of the first flip-flop, FF0, and each subsequent Q output is connected to the Ck input of the next flip-flop in line.

To analyse the action of a counter like this, it is essential to remember that each flip-flop toggles on the trailing edge of the

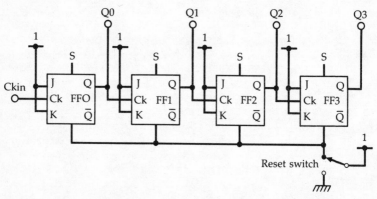

Figure 6.1 A four-bit asynchronous or ripple counter, using JK flip-flops

Ck1	Q0	Q1	Q2	Q3
0	0	0	0	0
1	0	0	0	0
0	1	0	0	0
1	1	0	0	0
0	0	1	0	0
1	0	1	0	0
0	1	1	0	0
1	1	1	0	0
0	0	0	1	0
1	0	0	1	0
0	1	0	1	0
1	1	0	1	0
0	0	1	1	0
1	0	1	1	0
0	1	1	1	0
1	1	1	1	0
0	0	0	0	1
1	0	0	0	1
0	1	0	0	1
1	1	0	0	1
0	0	1	0	1
1	0	1	0	1
0	1	1	0	1
1	1	1	0	1
0	0	0	1	1
1	0	0	1	1
0	1	0	1	1
1	1	0	1	1
0	0	1	1	1
1	0	1	1	1
0	1	1	1	1

Figure 6.2 The state table for the four-bit counter

clock pulse. The state of each output for a set of inputs is shown in Figure 6.2, assuming that the output shown is that following the change in the clock voltage. The outputs from the flip-flops follow the pattern of a binary count, in which Q3 is the most significant digit output and Q0 is the least significant digit output. The state of the outputs, in this example, shows the number of complete pulses at the input for a count range of 0 to 15, since there are only four bits of counter used.

The reason for the name *ripple* or *ripple through* can be seen from an inspection of the state table. At certain times in the count, the transition from 1 to 0 of the input pulse will cause a 1 to 0 transition of Q0, then a 1 to 0 transition of Q1 and so on. There is an inevitable time delay between these transitions, so that the change 'ripples through' the set of flip-flops, reaching the most significant digit some time after the original change at the input. This ripple through time can cause problems, as we shall see later, similar to the race hazard problems in gate circuits, and the solution lies in the use of a different type of counter, the synchronous counter.

The counter of Figure 6.1 is an up-counter, because the count increases by one binary digit for each complete pulse at the input. It is possible very easily to change this to a down-counter, in which the count number decreases by one digit for each input pulse. The circuit of a simple 4-stage down-counter is shown in Figure 6.3,

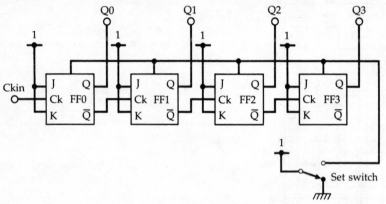

Figure 6.3 A four-bit down counter, obtained by using the NOT Q connections

and as you can see, the main difference is just that the NOT Q outputs rather than the Q outputs have been used for connecting to the next flip-flop. The outputs are still taken from the Q terminals, and we can ensure that the counter starts at its maximum count (denary 15) by using the set terminals in place of the reset terminals for the switched set operation.

Because the differences between up-counting and down-counting are so minor, it is possible to make combined up/down counters, in which the direction of counting can be reversed by altering the logic voltage on a terminal. This is achieved by using gating between the counter stages, and Figure 6.4 shows a typical example, with only two counter stages illustrated. The gating between stages consists of two AND gates and an OR, with one terminal of each AND gate connected to a gating line. One of the gating lines, usually the up line, is connected to a terminal, the other is driven from an inverter, and the terminal will be labelled to show the voltages that are needed, such as $U/\bar{D}$ indicating that

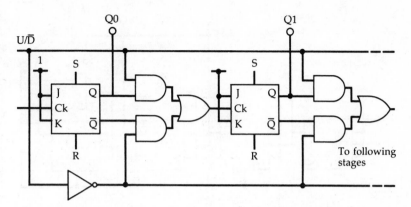

Figure 6.4 The gating that is used between stages for a switchable up/down counter

up-counting will take place if this terminal is at logic 1, and down counting if the voltage is logic 0. Circuits of this type are easily constructed in IC form, but the 74 series up/down counters are all of the synchronous type.

Incomplete counts

A counter using four flip-flops can work with the range 0 to 15, but for BCD work, a 0 −9 range is needed. Since a counter with three flip-flops can count only 0 to 7, we need to use four stages, and some method of resetting a counter on the next pulse following the count of 9 is needed in order to convert a four-stage counter to denary. The simplest method is to employ gating to detect the state caused by the tenth input pulse and use this to reset all stages of the counter, as illustrated in Figure 6.5. In practice, only the three higher digits need to be gated to detect the state 1010 (denary ten). Using Q3, NOT Q2 and Q1 into the NAND gate will cause the output to change to 0, so causing a complete reset of the whole counter.

This method of detecting a count state so as to force a reset allows asynchronous counters to be constructed for any count number, following the rule of providing enough flip-flops for the next higher power of two, and then gating the required output. When large count numbers are used at high speed, however, this can lead to problems because of the ripple-through nature of the synchronous counter. Suppose, for example, that we need to

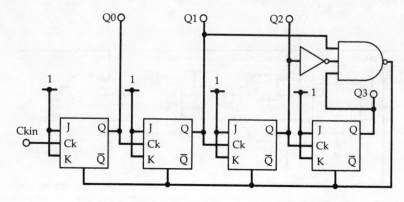

Gate detects 101X, which is reached at 1010

Figure 6.5 Limiting the count. In this example, the counter will reset when the count of denary 10 is reached

detect a state such as 100000000000000. When a pulse arrives this will change from 011111111111111 to this count number, the lowest bit will change first from 0 to 1, and the others will follow in turn. Now if we are gating, as seems reasonable, on the most significant and the least significant digits, then at a high pulse rate it is possible that by the time the most significant digit has changed from 0 to 1, the least significant digit which was 0 will have been changed by the next pulse back to 1, so that the gating cannot operate correctly. This form of race hazard is solved to some extent by the use of synchronous counters.

For applications in which gating is not used, however, asynchronous counters have an advantage for very fast input rates. In an asynchronous counter, only the first stage need run at the highest speed, the speed of the input pulses Each successive stage then works at half the rate of the stage preceding it, so that the inevitable stray capacitances in the IC are of less significance. A synchronous counter, as we shall see, uses the input clock pulse to feed each stage, loading this pulse source with a large amount of stray capacitance and also requiring each stage in the counter to operate at the fastest speed. Counters for purposes such as frequency meters for the VHF/UHF bands often use asynchronous stages made from ECL logic stages for a first high-speed stage, followed by more conventional synchronous or asynchronous stages for the lower rates at the output of the high-speed stage.

Gating the reset input is simple, but 'dirty' in the sense that it allows the count of denary ten to be reached, even if only momentarily, before the reset is achieved. A better method is to make use of the inputs J=0, K=1 which will reset each flip-flop at the instant when the clock pulse is received, and change the outputs at the trailing edge of the pulse. When this scheme is used, however, the gating system must detect the count of denary nine rather than ten, because it will be the tenth clock pulse that will initiate the change, not the achievement of a count of ten. Figure 6.6 shows how a scheme like this could be implemented for a

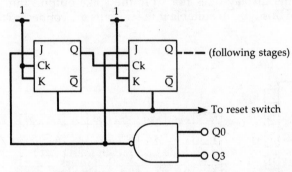

Figure 6.6 An alternative method of limiting the count. This uses the J and K inputs to determine what will happen on the tenth input, and has the advantage that the count of ten is never actually allowed to appear, even momentarily

decade counter. The count 1001, binary nine, has to be detected using a NAND gate whose output drives all of the J inputs. With the K inputs taken to level 1, states 0000 to 1000 have no effect on the NAND gate, so that the output is at level 1 and the flip-flops toggle. After the ninth clock pulse, however, the count has reached 1001, and the NAND gate output will switch to level 0, so that the tenth clock pulse will reset all of the flip-flops, due to the J=0, K=1 state. The count of 1010 is never reached, even momentarily. This method of terminating a count is preferable to that using the reset input, particularly for fast counts or large count numbers.

An interrupted count to nine, followed by resetting, however achieved, is the basis of BCD counters, in which each counter unit (a set of four flip-flops) is used for one column of a denary number. BCD counting allows for the display of a count number in denary rather than in binary, so that BCD counters are preferred for any application in which a count is to be displayed rather than simply used. BCD counters are available in IC form in the 74 series, and the simplest unit is the 7490. This is one of the few IC counters classed as asynchronous, and is designed mainly for use with displays. The design is, in fact, a split counter with one scale-of-two (a single flip-flop) and one scale of five which uses three flip-flops connected as a synchronous counter (see later in this chapter). For decade counting, the output of one unit is connected to the clock input of the other, so that the overall action is asynchronous. Because of the asynchronous action, the Q outputs will not change simultaneously, and this can give rise to spikes on the outputs. These are unimportant if the output is used to operate a display, since the display does not store the spike output, but make a counter of this type unsuitable if the outputs are connected to latches.

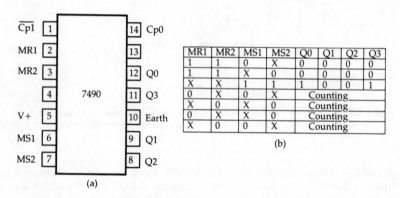

MR1	MR2	MS1	MS2	Q0	Q1	Q2	Q3
1	1	0	X	0	0	0	0
1	1	X	0	0	0	0	0
X	X	1	1	1	0	0	1
0	X	0	X	Counting			
X	0	X	0	Counting			
0	X	X	0	Counting			
X	0	0	X	Counting			

(b)

Figure 6.7 The pin diagram (a) and use table (b) for the 7490 type of ripple counter chip. Most IC counters make use of synchronous rather than asynchronous counting

The pinouts and the action of the controlling pins are shown in Figure 6.7. The pins labelled MR1 and MR2 are reset inputs which must both be taken to logic 1 to reset the counter, since they are inputs to a NAND gate. The inputs MS1 and MS2 are similarly used to set the most significant and least significant flip-flops to 1 (setting the count at 1001, denary 9). The counter is clocked by the trailing edge of the clock pulse. The maximum ripple delay, from the clock pulse input to the Q3 output, is of the order of 100 ns for standard TTL, but around 50 ns for the LS version of the chip.

Synchronous counting

The asynchronous or ripple counter was the first type of counter that was developed when discrete bistable circuits were used, and was extensively used along with clocked flip-flops of the R-S or D variety. The development of the JK type of flip-flop, however, makes it possible to construct, without too much circuit complication, a synchronous flip-flop in which the input pulses are connected to each clock input, and the change over of each unit is carried out by using the J and K inputs, with these connections determined in turn by gates. The design of a synchronous flip-flop involves rather more than the simple Q-to-Ck connection that we use in the asynchronous type, and the methods that are involved can best be appreciated if we start with as few stages as possible.

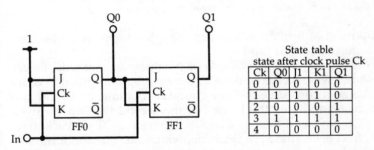

Ck	Q0	J1	K1	Q1
0	0	0	0	0
1	1	1	1	0
2	0	0	0	1
3	1	1	1	1
4	0	0	0	0

Figure 6.8 A two-stage synchronous counter. The first stage is a conventional toggling flip-flop, but the second makes use of switching the J and K inputs

Figure 6.8 shows a two-stage synchronous counter. The first flip-flop, FF0, is connected just as the first stage of an asynchronous counter would be, with both J and K inputs taken to logic 1. The clock pulse is, however, taken to both flip-flops, the trade-mark of a synchronous counter. The Q0 output is connected not to the second clock input but to the combined J and K inputs of FF1. The action is then as shown in the table, in which the states of Q0, J1, K1 and Q1 are shown as they are *after* each clock pulse, taking clock pulse 0 to mean the situation after resetting and before any clock pulse has arrived. The first flip-flop, FF0, then acts as a straightforward toggling device, and the output state of Q0 then determines whether FF1 shall toggle (J1=K1=1) or remain unchanged (J1=K1=0) when the next clock pulse arrives. The important point about any table like this is that the state of J and

125

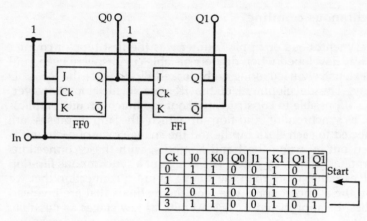

Figure 6.9 Altering the counting scale of a synchronous counter. In this case, the count is to denary 3, achieved by the connections shown

K inputs of a flip flop will determine what happens on the *next* clock pulse into that flip-flop.

As an equally simple example of synchronous methods, Figure 6.9 shows what has to be done to the two-flip-flop circuit in order to change it to a scale-of-three counter, counting 00, 01, 10 and then resetting. Only the J input of the second flip-flop is driven from Q0 now, and there is a connection from NOT Q1 back to J0. The effect is illustrated in the table, which shows a count from 00 to 10 followed by a reset to 00. The reset has, however, been accomplished by using the J and K inputs, and a separate asynchronous reset would be available using the R terminals of the flip-flops.

The design of a two-stage counter is not exactly strenuous, but it is important as a guide for later development. A good start to design is a state table, which shows in each line the present states of the outputs, the next state of the outputs and the J and K states that will be needed to achieve these changes. A table like this for the scale-of-three (Figure 6.10) shows that the K0 and K1 terminal

Present		Next		Necessary values			
Q0	Q1	Q0	Q1	J0	K0	J1	K1
0	0	1	0	1	1	0	1
1	0	0	1	1	1	1	1
0	1	0	0	0	1	0	1

Figure 6.10 A count table which shows present and next count state, so allowing the necessary J and K levels to be shown

126

voltages can be fixed at level 1, and that only J0 and J1 need to be variable. The table clearly shows that J0 is identical to NOT Q1, and that J1 is identical to Q0, so fixing the connections that have to be made in the counter. If the changes were to be more extensive, we might need to use Karnaugh maps to show what voltages we needed for each J and K input for each state of the Q outputs so that the change could be correctly made.

Present			Next			Necessary values			
Q2	Q1	Q0	Q2	Q1	Q0	J2	K2	J1	K1
0	0	0	0	0	1	0	X	0	X
0	0	1	0	1	0	0	X	1	X
0	1	0	0	1	1	0	X	X	0
0	1	1	1	0	0	1	X	X	1
1	0	0	1	0	1	0	X	0	X
1	0	1	1	1	0	0	X	1	X
1	1	0	1	1	1	0	X	0	X
1	1	1	0	0	0	X	1	X	1

$J0 = K0 = 1$ throughout

Figure 6.11 A count table for a three-stage synchronous counter. Only one value of J and K is ever important, so that the other can be shown as X, meaning *don't care*. This allows X to be used as either 1 or 0 in a Karnaugh map, simplifying the logic

To illustrate this, Figure 6.11 shows the state table for a three-stage counter of the synchronous type. In this example, the outputs have been arranged in Q2Q1Q0 sequence to make it easier to follow the binary count steps. Since the first stage is always a toggling one we do not need to show the J0K0 levels in this table as they will always be logic 1. Instead, we can concentrate on J1, K1, J2 and K2.

This table is not as straightforward as you might expect, because for a large number of changes, only a J or a K input needs to be at a definite voltage and the other can be either 1 or 0. Suppose, for example, that a Q output is to change from 0 to 1. This can be done with J=1, K=0 or with J=1, K=1, so that this could be shown as J=1, K=X where X means 'don't care', meaning either 1 or 0. This use of a don't care state makes the circuit of the counter considerably easier. For a change from 1 to 0, we can use J=X, K=1, for a non-change from 0 to 0 we can use J=0, K=X and for a non-change from 1 to 1 we can use J=X, K=0.

We can now start to determine what we need to do to establish the driving voltages to the J1, K1, J2 and K2 terminals. This *can* be done by inspecting the table, but it's better to use Karnaugh maps,

Q0Q1	Q2 0	1
00	0	0
01	X	0
11	X	X
10	1	1

J1 = Q0

Q0Q1	Q2 0	1
00	X	X
01	0	X
11	1	1
10	X	X

K1 = Q0

Q0Q1	Q2 0	1
00	0	0
01	0	0
11	1	X
10	0	0

J2 = Q0.Q1

Q0Q1	Q2 0	1
00	X	X
01	X	X
11	X	1
10	X	X

K2 = Q0.Q1

Figure 6.12 The Karnaugh maps for the J and K inputs, using the X lines to simplify the gating by making larger groupings

as shown in Figure 6.12. We shall need four Karnaugh maps, one for each J or K terminal, showing the 1, 0 or X states of that J or K terminal for each possible existing value (not *next* value) of Q0, Q1 and Q2. Filling in these tables needs some care because of the arrangement of the rows and columns. You need to remember in this case that the row sequence is 00, 01, 11 and 10, and that these are values of Q0Q1 and not, as you read from the state tables, Q1Q0.

Getting the gate requirements from the Karnaugh maps is not so simple as it is in combinational circuits in which each entry is 0 or 1. The X entries in this type of Karnaugh map can be taken as 0 or 1, and which you take is whatever makes the gating simplest. In the maps for J1 and K1, for example, taking the X entries adjacent to the 1 entries allows the gate condition to be simply J1 = K1 = Q0. In the J2 and K2 maps, taking the adjacent X as 1 allows the gating to be J2 = K2 = Q0.Q1. A further advantage here is that for both sets, the J and K voltages have been identical. This would not necessarily be the case if the three-stage counter had used a terminated count, terminating at 5 or 6, for example, instead of 7.

The final arrangement is shown in Figure 6.13, with a single AND gate used in the supply to J2, K2 to ensure the correct count. Once a three-stage counter has been understood, the design of synchronous counters with larger count numbers is less difficult providing that the count is the natural one, to the number 2^{n-1}, where n is the number of flip-flops. The four-stage counter is illustrated in Figure 6.14, with a further AND gate used to make the condition for J3 = K3 = 1 be Q0.Q1.Q2. This allows flip-flop 3 to be toggled when Q0 = Q1 = Q2 = 1 and the next clock pulse arrives, and subsequently the J = K = 0 state at this flip-flop will maintain the output steady until the next time that the gate output is high.

As many stages as you wish can be added in this way, using an AND gate to gate the output of a flip-flop with its own J and K

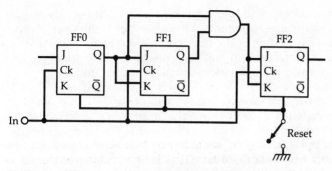

Figure 6.13 The circuit for the three-stage synchronous counter, with a reset line illustrated. The reset line would normally be held at logic 1 by a pull-up resistor, not shown

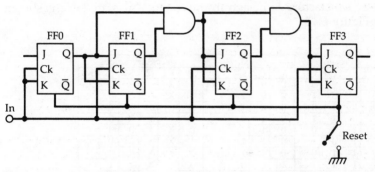

Figure 6.14 A four-stage synchronous counter, built on from the previous three-stage type

inputs, but for a long count, this introduces delays because of the need for changes to 'ripple through' the gates. This can be overcome by using multiple-input gates for each stage. In the four-stage illustration, for example, the gate supplying flip-flop 3 would have inputs from Q0, Q1 and Q2. A fifth stage would need to gate Q0, Q1, Q2 and Q3 together and so on. This use of multiple gating reduces rippling, but requires suitable gates, easy enough when the circuit is in IC form, but not when the circuit has to be constructed from 74-series units. However, with 13-input gates available, the practical restrictions are not too confining.

Difficulties arise mainly when a large and unusual count number is required, as for counters dealing in old Imperial measures like 56 lbs to a half-hundredweight. It's rather fortunate that the advance of electronics should have kept pace with the advance in the use of metric measurements, but this is not really coincidence, since the metric system is the only complete system of measuring units — the Imperial system has no units for any electrical quantities, so that any use of electricity involves metric units.

An example of design for an interrupted count is a decade counter, whose maximum count will be 1001. One way of implementing such a counter would be to make a conventional four-stage synchronous counter and gate it so that it resets on the tenth clock pulse, using the same gating system to detect 1010 as for the asynchronous scale-of-ten. This method is open to the same objections as before, that it allows the count of ten to exist, even momentarily, and we can make the count proceed without this type of reset if we make use of the JK gating. This *could* be done by modifying the gating of an existing four-stage counter, but it is more satisfactory to design from scratch. The state table is shown in Figure 6.15.

Present				Next				Necessary values					
Q3	Q2	Q1	Q0	Q3	Q2	Q1	Q0	J1	K1	J2	K2	J3	K3
0	0	0	0	0	0	0	1	0	X	0	X	0	X
0	0	0	1	0	0	1	0	1	X	0	X	0	X
0	0	1	0	0	0	1	1	X	0	0	X	0	X
0	0	1	1	0	1	0	0	X	1	1	X	0	X
0	1	0	0	0	1	0	1	0	X	X	0	0	X
0	1	0	1	0	1	1	0	1	X	X	0	0	X
0	1	1	0	0	1	1	1	X	0	X	0	0	X
0	1	1	1	1	0	0	0	X	1	X	1	1	X
1	0	0	0	1	0	0	1	0	X	0	X	X	0
1	0	0	1	0	0	0	0	0	X	0	X	X	1

Figure 6.15 The count table for a decade synchronous counter

Now from this state table, we need to work out the gating, and the Karnaugh maps are shown in Figure 6.16. These, apart from the gates for J1 and K1, are not so straightforward as the four-stage binary counter, and after this gating has been worked out, we still have to decide how to put it into practice. Figure 6.17 shows one possible implementation using four AND gates, all of which are two-input gates. This is a useful implementation from the practical point of view, since it permits the use of a quad 2-input AND gate, a standard unit, rather than having some 3-input gates, which would require more than one gate chip to be added.

As it happens, we do not need to design decade counters for ourselves in this way, and the design that has just been described

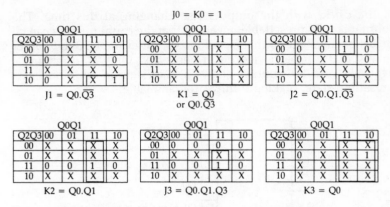

$J0 = K0 = 1$

Q2Q3	00	01	11	10
00	0	X	X	1
01	0	X	X	0
11	X	X	X	X
10	0	X	X	1

$J1 = Q0.\overline{Q3}$

(header: Q0Q1)

Q2Q3	00	01	11	10
00	X	0	X	1
01	X	X	X	X
11	X	X	X	X
10	X	0	1	X

$K1 = Q0$
or $Q0.\overline{Q3}$

(header: Q0Q1)

Q2Q3	00	01	11	10
00	0	0	1	0
01	0	X	0	0
11	X	X	X	X
10	X	X	X	X

$J2 = Q0.Q1.\overline{Q3}$

(header: Q0Q1)

Q2Q3	00	01	11	10
00	X	X	X	X
01	X	X	X	X
11	0	0	1	0
10	X	X	X	X

$K2 = Q0.Q1$

(header: Q0Q1)

Q2Q3	00	01	11	10
00	0	0	0	0
01	X	X	X	X
11	0	0	1	0
10	X	X	X	X

$J3 = Q0.Q1.Q3$

(header: Q0Q1)

Q2Q3	00	01	11	10
00	X	X	X	X
01	0	X	X	1
11	X	X	X	X
10	X	X	X	X

$K3 = Q0$

Figure 6.16 The Karnaugh maps for the gating of the decade counter

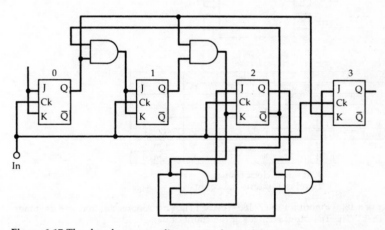

Figure 6.17 The decade counter diagram as obtained from the Karnaugh map analysis

is for illustration of the methods that need to be used for other non-binary counts. For decade counting with synchronous counters we would normally make use of an integrated unit such as the 74160 type. This is not so simple as the 7490 unit that we considered earlier. To start with, this is a totally synchronous counter, and its internal flip-flops are triggered at the *leading* edge of the clock, with the outputs also changing at this time. The counter is fully presettable, meaning that the count number can be preset at any stage so that a count from, for example, 3 to 9 rather than 0 to 9 can be carried out if necessary. Only an up-count is available, and the counter allows a hold state in addition to its presetting state, making it fully programmable.

(a)

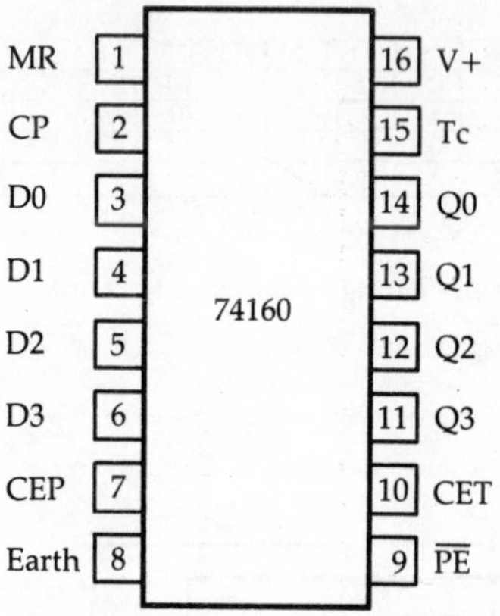

(b)

Mode	Inputs						Outputs	
	MR	CP	CEP	CET	PE	D	Q	Tc
Reset	0	X	X	X	X	X	0	0
Parallel load	1	↑	X	X	0	0	0	0
	1	↑	X	X	0	1	1	*
Count	1	↑	1	1	1	X	X	*
Hold	1	X	0	X	1	X	Qn	*
	1	X	X	0	1	X	Qn	0

↑ at 0 to 1 clock change
*Level is 1 at terminal count

Figure 6.18(a) Pinout for the 74160 type of TTL synchronous counter, and the mode table (b). The Tc output changes at the count of denary 10

Figure 6.18 shows the pin diagram of this unit, along with a table of pin functions. The MR input is a resetting input which is active when taken low and would normally be used shortly after power has been applied to the counter, before counting begins. This is an important point, because in any device that consists of a set of flip-flops, application of power will cause some flip-flops to set to a 1 output, other to reset to a 0 output. A counter cannot therefore be used immediately power has been applied; it must be reset before

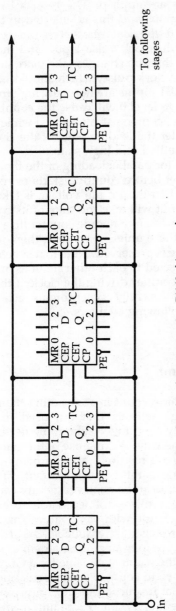

Figure 6.19 Connection outline for a five-decade counter using 74160 chips, and allowing for further stages to be added

any counting pulses are applied. The reset action, as usual, is completely asynchronous and this is reflected in the table by the X which means 1 or 0 (the *don't care* state).

The CP pin takes the clock pulse input, and the arrows in the table are a reminder that the changes take place on the leading (0 to 1) transition of the clock pulse, which should have a short rise time. The CEP and CET inputs are normally high for counting, but taking either or both to level 0 will cause the count output to hold its existing state. This action must *not* be used while the clock pulse input is low, only after the leading edge of the clock pulse when the clock input has settled to a high state.

The PE pin is used for parallel loading of the flip-flops, allowing a number to be preset before counting starts or re-starts. Parallel loading is enabled when the PE pin voltage is taken to 0, and in this state each Q output will take the state of its corresponding D input. Figure 6.19 shows a five-decade counter (to a count of 99999) which makes use of these units, connecting them together so that synchronous counting is preserved. Note that synchronous decade counters *can* be connected to each other in an asynchronous way, with the output of a counter driving the clock of the next, but the circuit shown preserves fully synchronous action, using one counter to gate the following counters.

Other forms of count

Suppose that we want to count in scales other than 8-4-2-1 binary or BCD? The gating methods that are used for synchronous counters allow for any counting system to be used, and design is carried out in the same way, making use of the state table to show what J and K entries are required, and Karnaugh maps to show what gating can achieve this. The important difference is that whereas a binary count can be achieved to any count number by repeating a basic design, this is not necessarily true of other types, and unless you can work with very large Karnaugh maps, a practical limit of four stages is reasonable. As it happens, most unorthodox counters are four-stage counters in any case.

Figure 6.20 shows the count state table for a Gray code counter. This view of a Gray code count reveals regularities that are not apparent from a casual inspection of the count numbers, and in particular you can see that the J and K requirements follow a very interesting pattern. The J0K0 set, in fact, simply follows a 101010...

Present				Next				Necessary values							
Q3	Q2	Q1	Q0	Q3	Q2	Q1	Q0	J0	K0	J1	K1	J2	K2	J3	K3
0	0	0	0	0	0	0	1	1	X	0	X	0	X	0	X
0	0	0	1	0	0	1	1	X	0	1	X	0	X	0	X
0	0	1	1	0	0	1	0	X	1	X	0	0	X	0	X
0	0	1	0	0	1	1	0	0	X	X	0	1	X	0	X
0	1	1	0	0	1	1	1	1	X	X	0	X	0	0	X
0	1	1	1	0	1	0	1	X	0	X	1	X	0	0	X
0	1	0	1	0	1	0	0	X	1	0	X	X	0	0	X
0	1	0	0	1	1	0	0	0	X	0	X	X	0	1	X
1	1	0	0	1	1	0	1	1	X	0	X	X	0	X	0
1	1	0	1	1	1	1	1	X	0	1	X	X	0	X	0
1	1	1	1	1	1	1	0	X	1	X	0	X	0	X	0
1	1	1	0	1	0	1	0	0	X	X	0	X	1	X	0
1	0	1	0	1	0	1	1	1	X	X	0	0	X	X	0
1	0	1	1.	1	0	0	1	X	0	X	1	0	X	X	0
1	0	0	1	1	0	0	0	X	1	0	X	0	X	X	0
1	0	0	0	0	0	0	0	0	X	0	X	0	X	X	1

Figure 6.20 The count table for a Gray code counter, using synchronous methods

sequence like the output of a binary counter stage, and subsequent JK inputs follow a pattern of equal numbers of 10 and 01 levels. This means that a Gray code counter could be constructed by making a binary counter, presetting it with a number that would give the correct starting conditions, and then using its outputs (fed from the same input) to supply the J and K inputs for the Gray code counter.

This regularity in the J and K states, however, does not make the gating of a Gray-code counter any easier. Figure 6.21 shows the Karnaugh maps and the resulting logic statements for the gates. The J0 and K0 conditions are the most difficult, but the later gates give rise to simpler statements, mainly because of the large number of don't care states. Figure 6.22 shows the gating that is needed for a four-stage counter — the actual counter stages are not shown. A diagram like this is more complicated than the circuit, because once a quantity has been gated (for example, in the XOR or XNOR gate) it can be connected to other gates that use this quantity. The XOR and XNOR actions have been used in place of AND/OR functions to make the design simpler to build.

Johnson counters

The Johnson counter is a design that has some peculiar advantages for specialised purposes. Like the Gray code, it makes use of a

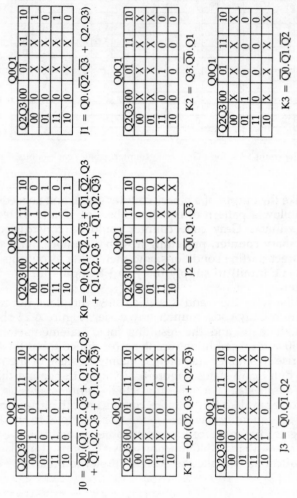

Figure 6.21 The Karnaugh maps for the J and K inputs of the Gray code counter

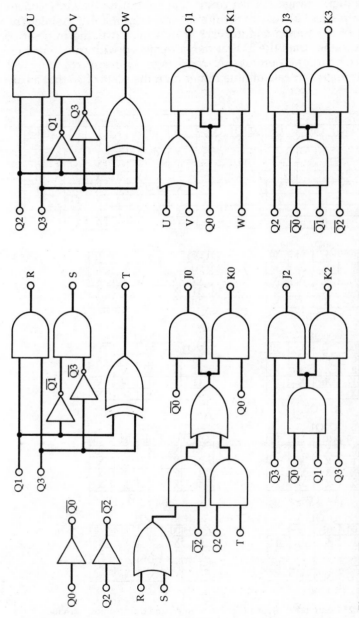

Figure 6.22 The gating for the Gray code counter. The gates are shown in logical arrangement rather than in physical or circuit arrangement

137

single digit change at each count change, but unlike Gray code it does not make full use of the number of states that is possible. The count of a Johnson counter is $2 \times n$, where n is the number of stages, rather than the 2^n that can be achieved with true binary (8-4-2-1 or Gray) counters. A four-stage Johnson counter will therefore give a scale of nine rather than the scale of 16 that a true

Present				Next				Necessary values								(a)
Q3	Q2	Q1	Q0	Q3	Q2	Q1	Q0	J0	K0	J1	K1	J2	K2	J3	K3	
0	0	0	0	1	0	0	0	0	X	0	X	0	X	1	X	
1	0	0	0	1	1	0	0	0	X	0	X	1	X	X	0	
1	1	0	0	1	1	1	0	0	X	1	X	X	0	X	0	
1	1	1	0	1	1	1	1	1	X	X	0	X	0	X	0	
1	1	1	1	0	1	1	1	X	0	X	0	X	0	X	1	
0	1	1	1	0	0	1	1	X	0	X	0	X	1	0	X	
0	0	1	1	0	0	0	1	X	0	X	1	0	X	0	X	
0	0	0	1	0	0	0	0	X	1	0	X	0	X	0	X	

(b)

Q0Q1

Q2Q3	00	01	11	10
00	0	X	X	X
01	0	X	X	X
11	0	1	X	X
10	X	X	X	X

$J0 = Q1$

Q0Q1

Q2Q3	00	01	11	10
00	X	X	0	1
01	X	X	X	X
11	X	X	0	X
10	X	X	0	X

$K0 = \overline{Q1}$

Q0Q1

Q2Q3	00	01	11	10
00	0	X	X	0
01	0	X	X	X
11	1	X	X	X
10	X	X	X	X

$J1 = Q2$

Q0Q1

Q2Q3	00	01	11	10
00	X	X	1	X
01	X	X	X	X
11	X	0	0	X
10	X	X	0	X

$K1 = \overline{Q2}$

Q0Q1

Q2Q3	00	01	11	10
00	0	X	0	0
01	1	X	X	X
11	X	X	X	X
10	X	X	X	X

$J2 = Q3$

Q0Q1

Q2Q3	00	01	11	10
00	X	X	X	X
01	X	X	X	X
11	0	0	0	X
10	X	X	1	X

$K2 = \overline{Q3}$

Q0Q1

Q2Q3	00	01	11	10
00	1	X	0	0
01	X	X	X	X
11	X	X	X	X
10	X	X	0	X

$J3 = \overline{Q0}$

Q0Q1

Q2Q3	00	01	11	10
00	X	X	X	X
01	0	X	X	X
11	0	0	1	X
10	X	X	X	X

$K3 = Q0$

Figure 6.23 Count table (a) for a Johnson counter, and the resulting Karnaugh maps (b). This action can also be achieved by the use of a shift register

binary counter can provide. The Johnson numbers always consist of a block of 1's and a block of 0's with no alternation of digits.

A Johnson count for a four-stage counter is shown in Figure 6.23(a), along with the J and K conditions (b) for a synchronous counter. The Karnaugh maps contain large blocks of don't care states, which allows for very simple decoding, as shown in Figure 6.24 for a four-stage counter. A counter of this type can be

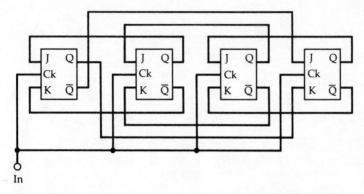

Figure 6.24 The connections required for a four-stage Johnson counter

implemented also by using shift registers, as indicated in Chapter 7, and is then known as a 'twisted ring counter' because it contains one connection of Q to K and NOT Q to J among a set of Q to J, NOT Q to K connections.

The ability to create any count sequence is the most valuable feature of synchronous counters using JK flip-flops, and the methods that have been illustrated in this chapter can be applied to any count type provided that it does not lead to Karnaugh maps that contain too many variables. As it happens, most established counting scales present no problems, but you might want to use some very odd scales indeed. Digital to analogue conversion from BCD, for example, might require a counter that gave, for counts of 0 to 9, a number of 1's equal to the count number (five 1's for 5, eight 1's for 8 and so on). This is a modifiction of the Johnson idea which requires one flip-flop for each 1. This would normally be considered rather wasteful of devices, but if it's the easier way out of a problem then it will be worth doing. Though the 74 series of ICs contains a large variety of counters, there is always likely to be an application for unusual designs for particular needs, and for such actions, the construction of a synchronous counter using JK flip-flops is often the simplest solution that involves the least amount of hardware. For a system that incorporates a microprocessor, of course, the simplest solution may be one that makes use of software along with the existing hardware.

7 Registers and memory

The PIPO register

A register is a set of flip-flops, each of which can hold a 1 or 0 at its output until this condition is changed. A register can further be described as being a *shift* register, meaning that a 1 present at one output can be shifted to the output of an adjacent flip-flop. The shift can be left, to a more significant place, or right to a less significant place. Like counters, registers can be constructed from flip-flops, of which the JK flip-flop, being the most versatile type, is the favourite device. Like counters, registers are available ready-made in IC form.

The only non-shift type of register is the parallel-in, parallel-out (PIPO) type which is illustrated in Figure 7.1. This uses the JK flip-flops as if they were D-types, and D-type flip-flops could just as easily be substituted in this circuit. The data bits at inputs D0–D3 can be changing, but at the moment of the clock pulse they will be latched to the output. The output will then remain stored until the next clock pulse, so that this type of register serves as a memory circuit holding a number of bits. The main use of the PIPO register is to act in this way as a holding store for data, particularly between devices that operate at very different speeds. For example, if an input is to be supplied to a digital circuit from a set of manually operated switches it would be undesirable normally to allow each switch to affect the action of the circuit until all of the switches have been operated. This can be done by making the switches supply the inputs to a PIPO register, and then applying a clock pulse to the register (by way of a push-button switch and a monostable) to latch the inputs to the output.

The same argument applies to a fast-acting digital circuit which has a set of outputs to a display or a printer. The duration of the

141

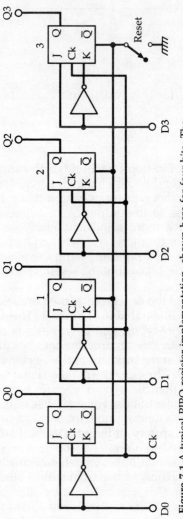

Figure 7.1 A typical PIPO register implementation, shown here for four bits. The use of 8-bit registers is more common

output might be of the order of microseconds, much too brief to see or to print, so that the output must be held in a PIPO register and the clock pulses to the register then gated off until the data has been dealt with. The type of arrangement that is made for clocking the PIPO register in applications like this is part of a general arrangement called 'handshaking'. In a handshaking system, one part of the circuit places data in the register and sends out a pulse to notify other parts (inputs, printers, displays etc.) that data is present. These other parts of the system then read the data in the register, send a pulse to the main system to acknowledge this, then await the return of a pulse which will signal that a further amount of data has been placed in the register. This type of system usually makes use of the interrupt system of a microprocessor, see Chapter 8.

PISO and SIPO

Two register types allow data to be converted between parallel and serial form. Parallel data is binary data that is present on several lines, with one bit of data on each line. Serial data is transmitted along a single line, with one different bit of data being on the line at each clock pulse. The main advantage of a serial system is that it allows data to be sent along single lines, such as telephone lines and radio links, and at one time serial data transmission was used extensively for connecting computers to printers and keyboards. The much higher speeds that can be attained (with fewer complications) by using parallel lines have now made this the normal method of transmitting data, with serial links used only where the use of a single line is essential.

The outline of a parallel-in serial-out (PISO) register is shown in Figure 7.2. The flip-flops are connected together with each Q output to the next J inputs and each NOT Q to the K input. The clock inputs are connected together to be driven from a common source, and inputs are made through the set and reset inputs of the JK flip-flops. The parallel inputs, D0 to D4 in this example, can be used irrespective of the state of the clock pulse, but at each clock pulse, the data at the output of a flip-flop is copied to the next flip-flop to the right because of the Q - J and NOT Q - K connections. At the end of the line, the bit which exists at the serial output, *Sout* will be replaced by the bit which was previously stored in FF2. A new bit is therefore available at the serial output for each clock

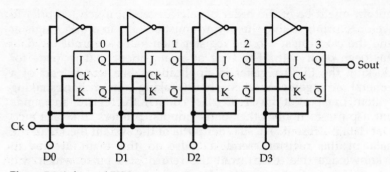

Figure 7.2 A form of PISO register, allowing parallel entry by way of the S and R inputs, and serial output at each clock pulse

pulse, so that this output can be connected to a line to permit serial data transmission.

If this serial data transmission is an internal part of a system, then the clock rate can be as fast as the characteristics of the line (its length, inductance and capacitance) permit, but for equipment that must interface with other digital equipment, the clocking rate for the serial output should conform to accepted standards. One of the standard clock rates, Figure 7.3, should be used, and the

Rates in bits per second
Note that the values shown are not all of the possible values, but those that are most widely used. Figures below 1200 are used only when noisy lines force such slow rates.

75	110	150	300	600
1200	2400	4800	9600	19200

Figure 7.3 The standard serial rates in bits per second. These are the rates used for external transfer (for example, from one computer to another), and higher rates can be used internally

signal should be asynchronous, see Appendix B. Most equipment that makes use of serial signals is stated to use RS-232, but this means little unless qualified by further information, because the old RS-232 standards are widely ignored. A true RS-232 signal uses levels of +15V and −15V for 1 and 0 levels respectively, but the use of these levels is now very unusual, and the normal digital 0V and +5V levels are much more common. Systems using these levels can be described as conforming to RS-432, but the older term is more often used.

What this means is that when devices are stated to use RS-232, the only thing that can be taken for granted is that they use serial data transmission. Though the original RS-232 specification stipulated a D-type plug and socket and the nature of connections to it, both the connector and the connections are ignored by some manufacturers. The main problem is that the RS-232 standards are by now totally out of date, and each manufacturer of equipment has contributed some different updating feature. Before connecting serial devices and expecting them to work, then, the circuit connections have to be checked, and also the clock rate and the method of transmission that is used. Until new standards can be devised and applied, this is all that can be done. Note that the use of parallel-loading and shifting does not imply that the output *must* be serial, because this type of register can be used for multiplication by a shift-and-add method.

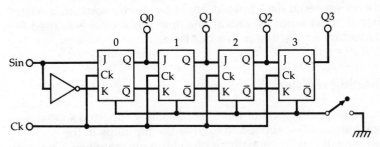

Figure 7.4 A SIPO register with asynchronous reset

The reverse of PISO is serial in, parallel out, or SIPO, and Figure 7.4 shows the system in outline. The serial line is connected to the J input of the first flip-flop, with an inverter used to connect in to the K input, and the flip-flops in the register are connected in shifting mode, Q to J and NOT Q to K. After resetting, the outputs will all be at zero, and at the first clock pulse after resetting, the Q0 output will latch the first bit at the input. At each clock pulse, a serial bit of data on the input line will be latched to Q0, and the former bit at Q0 will be shifted to Q1, and so on. After as many clock pulses as there are flip-flops in the register, four in this example, the outputs will represent a set of inputs and can be read, followed by resetting so that a new set can be read.

This action is the exact opposite of the PISO register, so that a serial link consists of a PISO register at one end and a SIPO register at the other. The way that JK flip-flops can be used means that it

145

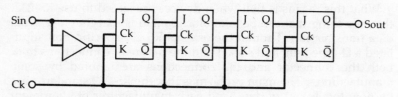

Figure 7.5 A SISO register, used mainly as a time delay

is possible to construct registers that can be used in both ways, and ICs of this type, with a few other features added, are known as SIO (serial input/output) *ports*.

The serial in, serial out (SISO) register of Figure 7.5 is used mainly as a time delay. A bit which is present on the input line at some point will be available on the output line after a number of clock pulses equal to the number of flip-flops, four in this example. This allows serial data to be delayed by a time equal to a whole number of clock pulses, and at one time this system was used for data storage of the first-in last-out type.

Counting registers

Since a register is a set of flip-flops, usually connected so that one clock pulse can be applied to each of the flip-flops in the register, each register is potentially a synchronous counter. Counters constructed from registers, however, are not the normal type of binary counter but more usually the one-digit-per-device type, as illustrated in Figure 7.6. This shows a set of flip-flops connected

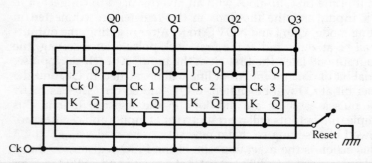

Figure 7.6 A straight-ring counter circuit using a SIPO register. The register must be set up with one 1 bit, since it cannot count if all outputs are zero

146

in the usual Q to J, NOT Q to K, mode, and with a reset arrangement which resets all but one of the flip-flops, placing a logic 1 into the other remaining flip-flop. After resetting, each clock pulse will then circulate that 1 by one place to the right and so back to the first flip-flop again. This is not a binary count, and the number scale that is used depends on the number of flip-flops that are connected in this way, a 'straight ring' connection.

A denary counter can be made using ten flip-flops in each decade, with the zero output used to pass a pulse to the next (higher order) set. This allows pulses to be counted with a direct output to simple display devices, like lamps set behind numbers on transparent disks. Counters like this are more useful for non-denary systems, however, since there are ample denary counters in IC form available. Ring counters come into their own where counts of 3, 4, 7, 9, 12 and others are required along with simple display devices. The straight ring counter requires as many flip-flops as there are digits in the count, ten for denary, five for a scale of 5 and so on.

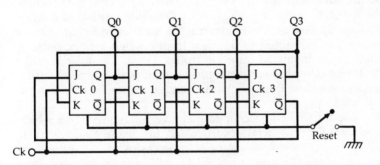

Figure 7.7 A twisted-ring (Johnson) counter

Figure 7.7 shows a twisted-ring (Johnson) counter, a type that has already been mentioned. In this counter type, the normal Q to J and NOT Q to K connections are made between flip-flops, but there is one external Q to K and NOT Q to J connection, the twisted connection. This gives rise to the count table as shown in Figure 7.8 for the four flip-flop counter, which is a scale of eight. Using a twisted ring allows the use of fewer flip-flops for a given scale, but the decoding of the count is not so simple and direct as that of the straight ring counter.

Pulse No.	Q0	Q1	Q2	Q3	Q̄3
0	0	0	0	0	1
1	1	0	0	0	1
2	1	1	0	0	1
3	1	1	1	0	1
4	1	1	1	1	0
5	0	1	1	1	0
6	0	0	1	1	0
7	0	0	0	1	0
8	0	0	0	0	1

Figure 7.8 The count table for the twisted-ring counter. Note that, unlike the straight-ring counter, no set-up bit is needed

Other devices

There is a whole family of devices which is constructed around a MOS device, the charge-coupled device. These are available in IC form only, and often as rather specialised packages, but they need to be included here for the sake of presenting a complete picture of the register family of devices. A CCD device consists of a set of MOS capacitors which are constructed so that the charge on a capacitor can be shifted to the next in line when a clock pulse is applied to an insulated gate electrode. The clock pulse usually consists of a two-phase or three-phase set of pulses applied to sets of gate electrodes. Both N-channel and P-channel CCDs can be constructed.

One use for CCD devices is to make very large registers which can be used for time delays; particularly for digital audio circuits. Another very prominent use is as pickup devices for miniature video cameras, charging each CCD cell from a light-sensitive material and using the shifting to read a line of cells so as to give a video output. Both uses are specialised and CCDs do not form a normal circuit component for digital circuit designers other than for some time delay applications.

Memory principles

The action of a register in retaining a bit which may have existed only momentarily on a line is the memory action, and some types of computer memory are based on registers. Since a register operates only when power is supplied to the ICs, memory of this type retains data only for as long as power is maintained, and is known as volatile memory to distinguish it from memory based on magnetic materials, non-volatile memory. Any form of memory that is based on registers will necessarily consume power, and the limitation to the size of a memory of this type will be the power dissipation, since an IC has very limited capabilities for dissipating heat. The use of a register form of memory is therefore not so common in small computers as an alternative that we shall examine later.

The register, used as a temporary memory, is also an important feature of a microprocessor chip, and this is one of the actions that we shall examine in Chapter 8. The distinction that is made between the terms *register* and *memory* is one of scale. We refer to a register when the contents of the flip-flops consist of a number of bits equal to the normal working group used in the computer or digital device, if the normal working group is a byte, a set of eight bits, then 8-bit registers will be used. The other common sizes are 16-bit and 32-bit. Memory, by contrast, deals with much larger numbers ranging from 1024 bits per chip to 262144 bits (256K) and higher per chip. The other important feature of memory is that it should be possible to gain access to some specified bit or set of bits, preferably without the need to gain access to any others, a feature that was absent in the earliest types of memory using registers. By contrast, the contents of a register are almost always dealt with as a whole, other than for a very few actions, called *bitwise* actions.

The earliest type of register memory was simply a SISO type of register that used a large number of flip-flops. Data was fed into the register by clocking, and was fed out in the same way. To avoid loss of data, each output (reading) operation used a number of clock pulses equal to the number of flip-flops in the register, and the output of the serial register was connected back to the input, so restoring all the data to the same positions after reading. A counter and gate circuit ensured that the correct portion of the data was made available to the external circuits. For example, if the register consisted of 1024 flip-flops (a typical size) and data from numbers 512 to 639 inclusive were wanted, the counting system would be set to open an output gate at bit 512 and close it again after bit 639, with 1024 clock pulses being used in all. The bits that were read would be placed into parallel registers for use.

Read/write memory of this type was used for a short time in the development of small computers, but is unsuitable for large memory requirements. The development of small computers depended on better memory devices, because the magnetic type of memory core that was established for large (mainframe) computers was physically much too large for small machines, and its memory capacity was not, by modern standards, particularly large though its response speed was, and still is, impressive. The main need, however, was for memory in IC form that allowed random access, access to any stored bit without disturbing any other part of the memory. The principles were well understood, and all that was needed was the development of the techniques for making ICs with a very large number of active components in each chip.

The essential feature of any random-access memory is *addressing*. Each bit is stored in a memory unit, which can be a flip-flop or (see later) a capacitor. That memory unit is numbered, using binary, and placing this number on a set of inputs (the address inputs) will give access to the unit for reading or writing. Address decoding is a comparatively simple gating action but its use on a memory chip of even modest size demands the construction of a large number of gates. A 1024-bit chip requires 1024 address numbers to be decoded so that each of the 1024 flip-flops in the chip can be connected to inputs for writing and/or outputs for reading. The address decoding portion of the chip is therefore likely to be as large as or larger than the actual storage portion. Large-scale memory was therefore not possible until IC techniques permitted the fabrication of at least tens of thousands of active devices, almost invariably MOS devices, per chip. The use of high densities of active devices demands the use of MOS in order to keep dissipation down to reasonable levels. The unit of memory capacity is the K, meaning 1024 bits rather than 1000, because 1024 is an exact power of two, 2^{10}.

Memory based on random access became known as random-access memory, shortened to RAM, and this name has stuck even though it is no longer really appropriate. Virtually all memory nowadays is random-access, and the name could be applied to any type of memory. It is, however, reserved for one type only, the type that can be written as well as read and which should be called RWM, read/write memory.

A read/write memory chip consists of the following:

1 A set of storage devices, such as flip-flops, with inputs and outputs.

2 An address decoder which can connect each input and output with external pins.

3 A selecting gate which can control whether an input (write) or an output (read) will be performed.

and such a system is critically dependent on power being applied, because when power is switched off, the output of the storage device will always be zero. It is possible, however, to fabricate memory using CMOS techniques, and retain data for very long periods, particularly if a low-voltage backup battery can be used. Such CMOS RAM is used extensively in calculators, and has also featured as an add-on for small computers. For the most part, however, RAM is volatile, and the main divisions are into static and dynamic forms.

Static RAM is based on using a flip-flop as each storage bit element. The state of a flip flop can remain unaltered until it is deliberately changed, or until power is switched off, and this made static RAM the first choice for manufacturers in the early days of IC memory. The snag is that power consumption can be large, even with MOS devices, because each flip-flop will draw current whether it stores a 0 or a 1. This has led to static RAM, except for the CMOS variety, being used only for comparatively small memory sizes. The predominant type of RAM technology for large memory sizes then became the dynamic RAM, since this allowed the construction of very large memory sizes along with very low power consumption and fast access. The use of CMOS memory has always resulted in slower access times than could be obtained using other devices, so that this type of memory is used mainly where it is essential, for battery-operated circuitry.

The dynamic RAM makes no use of flip-flops other than in its address selecting circuits. Each storage cell in this type of RAM consists of a miniature MOS capacitor. Logic 0 is represented by a discharged capacitor, logic 1 by a charged capacitor. Since the capacitor element can be very small, it is possible to construct very large RAM memory chips ($64K \times 1$ bit, $128K \times 1$ bit, and $256K \times 1$ bit are now quite common), and the power requirements of the capacitor are very small. The snag is that a small MOS capacitor will not retain charge for much longer than a millisecond, since the capacitor will inevitably leak. All dynamic memory chips must therefore be 'refreshed', meaning that each address which contains a logic 1 must be re-charged at intervals of no more than a millisecond. The refreshing action can be carried out within the chip, providing that the cycling of address numbers is done externally.

Some microprocessor chips provide for this memory refreshing to be carried out on any memory chips that are connected to them, others require the use of additional refresh circuitry, often provided in chip form by manufacturers of memory. The availability of very large capacity dynamic memory chips has caused the price of RAM (expressed as cents per kilobyte) to fall dramatically for a considerable period. Over the same period, the reliability of dynamic RAM, which at one time was suspect, has improved so as to be on a par with any other IC components. It is this development in dynamic RAM technology which more than any other single factor, has been responsible for the simultaneous drop in prices and rise in memory size of small computers over the past few years. More recently, improvements in CMOS technology have resulted in large sizes of static RAM chips which need no refreshing. The problem of early CMOS designs, slow operation, has been overcome, and the slightly higher cost of modern static RAM is balanced by the lack of any need for refresh circuitry.

Fixed memory

The use of read/write memory, or RAM, is an essential part of memory action in digital circuits, but not the only part. It is equally important to have memory whose content is fixed, unalterable, and therefore called 'read-only' memory, or ROM. Random-access will be required to read this ROM, which is why the name is so inappropriate for read/write memory. The important feature of ROM is that it is non-volatile, meaning that the stored bits are unaffected by switching off power to the memory, and are available for use whenever power is restored. If there must be an output available from the memory whenever it is switched on, ROM is essential. ROM is therefore a feature of many types of digital circuits that require memory, and is indispensable to any microprocessor application; in some applications it might be the only type of memory that is needed.

The simplest type of such a ROM consists of permanent connections to logic 0 or logic 1 voltage lines, as Figure 7.9 indicates. In this diagram, two AND gates are shown, with one input of each tied to a fixed voltage. When the gates are enabled by the enable lines, gate A output will be at logic 0, and the gate B output will be at logic 1 because of the fixed connections at the inputs. We can develop this idea into the system shown in Figure 7.10, in which eight gates feed into a common output line. One input of each gate is held at a fixed level, either 0 or 1, and the other input is used as an enable, fed from a demultiplexer, a gate circuit which gives a voltage on one of a set of output lines in response to a binary input. In this way, the three lines into the

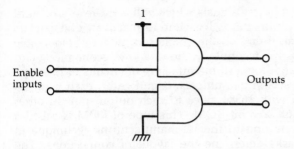

Figure 7.9 The basis of a ROM chip is permanent connections to level 1 or 0, connected to outputs by way of gates

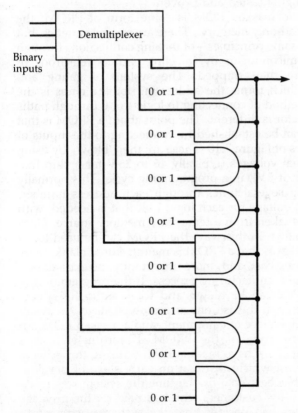

Figure 7.10 Selecting which of a set of gates levels will appear at an output. This uses a demultiplexer (a form of ring counter) which will give a 1 at the appropriate output for a binary input (the *address*), in this case on three lines

demultiplexer carry binary signals which will activate any of eight lines out. These output lines will each in turn activate one gate, so passing one signal, 0 or 1 to the single output. The remarkable developments in IC technology now allow economical and comparatively straightforward manufacture of circuits of this type which have eight sets of demultiplexers and gates, each using 14 address lines and with 16384 gates to each output pin. In other words, this is a 16K × 8 bit ROM. This type of ROM is called a 'masked' ROM, referring to the IC manufacturing technique in which etching masks determine the layout of connections. The masks form the main initial cost of production of such a ROM, and the use of masked ROM is feasible only if the content of this memory is thoroughly tested and proven.

An alternative to masked ROM is some form of PROM, the 'programmable read-only memory'. There are several varieties, but nearly all use the same principles — of making connections through lightly doped semiconductor by injecting carriers (electrons or holes), which are then trapped. The system of gating and demultiplexing which forms the addressing for the chips is the same, only the method of connecting to logic 1 or 0 through paths in the semiconductor is different. The point about a PROM is that the connections can be established by connecting to the inputs of gates like the gates of Figure 7.10. These are then 'blown' by using higher than normal voltages (typically 16 to 25 V for a chip that normally operates at 5 V), in a programming cycle. This normally consists of cycling several times through each address number, applying the high voltage for each logic 1 bit that is needed, with the correct signals taken from a temporary memory source. Once programmed or blown in this way, the PROM can be used like a ROM. The advantage is that a PROM is manufactured blank, there is no special masking cost, and, more importantly, no extra design time needed in the manufacturing process. If the programming is faulty, new PROMS can be blown and tried, until the system seems to be bug free. If this is done at prototype stage, the result can be a very reliable piece of equipment, and a masked ROM can be made from any copy of the PROM. Unfortunately, some computer manufacturers have made a habit of using this scheme to release equipment which is still at an early stage of development. The result has been that by the time the system was ready for masked ROMs, the customers who had paid for the privilege of finding the bugs had decided that the system wasn't worth having.

Using PROMs is a short term expedient, but one which is useful in that short term. Though PROM chips are expensive, they can be re-used, apart from the 'fusible link' type in which the internal connections are opened permanently during the blowing process. The most popular type of PROM is erasable by shining UV light into the silicon whose conductivity establishes the logic 1 connections. The effect of UV is to make the material conductive to such an extent that the trapped charges can move, making the material into an insulator. This process is described as 'washing', and typically takes an exposure of 5 minutes to 30 minutes, depending on the construction of the PROM and the wavelength of UV. The most effective UV for the purpose is the shorter wavelength type, and this radiation must not be allowed to reach any part of a human body, particularly the eyes. PROM-washers must therefore be constructed in light-tight boxes, with interlock switches to eliminate the possibility of the light being on when the box is open.

Bus connections

Bus is the name that is given to a set of shared lines in a digital circuit, particularly a microprocessor circuit. The three main buses of a microprocessor circuit are the address bus, the data bus, and the control bus. The name 'bus' is a throwback to the original Latin *omnibus*, meaning 'for all'. The buses of a microprocessor system consist of lines that are connected to each and every part of the system, so that signals are made available at many chips simultaneously. Since understanding the bus action is vitally important to understanding the action of any memory system, we'll concentrate on each bus in turn, starting with the address bus.

An address bus consists of the lines that connect between the microprocessor address pins and each of the memory chips in the microprocessor system. In anything but a very simple system, the address bus would connect to other units also, but for the moment we'll ignore these other connections, and also the methods by which binary numbers are placed on the bus lines. A typical older style 8-bit microprocessor would use 16 address pins. Using the relationship that n pins allow 2^n binary number combinations, the use of 16 address lines permits 65536 memory addresses to be used. In general, memory chips nowadays are 'one-bit' types, which allow only one bit of data to be stored per address. For an 8-bit microprocessor, then, the simplest RAM layout would consist of eight 64K × 1-bit chips, each of which would be connected to

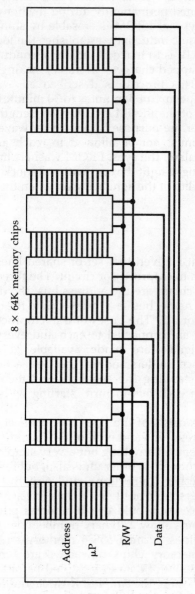

Figure 7.11 Using 64K memory chips of one stored bit per chip to form a complete 64K × 8-bit memory

8 × 64K memory chips

Address

μP

R/W

Data

all 16 lines of the address bus. Each of these chips would then contribute one bit of data, so that each chip is connected to a different line of the data bus.

This scheme is illustrated in Figure 7.11. At each of the 65536 possible address numbers, each chip will give access to one bit, and this access is provided through the lines of the data bus. The combination of address bus and data bus provides for addressing and the flow of data, but another line is needed to determine the direction of data. This extra line is the read/write line, one of the lines of the *control bus*. When the read/write line is at one logic level, the signal at each memory chip transfers all connections to the inputs of the memory units, so that the memory is written with whatever bit is present on the data line. If the read/write signal changes to the opposite logic level, then the internal gating in the memory chips connects to the output of each memory cell rather than to the input, making the logic level of the cell affect the data line. The provision of address bus, data bus and read/write line will therefore be sufficient to allow the microprocessor to work with 64K of memory in this example. For smaller amounts of memory, the only change to this scheme is that some of the address lines of the address bus are not used. These unused lines must be the higher-order lines, starting at the most significant line. For a 16-line address bus, the most significant line is the A15 line, the least significant is the A0.

A memory system that consisted purely of 64K of RAM, however, would not be useful, because no program would be present at switch-on to operate the microprocessor. There must be some ROM present, even if it is a comparatively small quantity. For some control applications, the whole of the programming might use only ROM, and the system would consist of one ROM chip connected to all of the data bus lines, and as many of the address lines as were needed to address the chip fully. As an example, Figure 7.12 shows what would be needed in this case, using an 8K × 8-bit ROM, which needs only the bottom 12 address lines. It's more realistic to assume that a system will need both ROM and RAM, and we now have to look at how these different sets of memory can be addressed. In the early days, the total addressing capability of an 8-bit machine was no particular restriction, and a common configuration was of 16K ROM and 16K RAM.

This could be achieved by 'mapping' the memory as shown in Figure 7.13—other combinations are, of course, possible. In the scheme that is illustrated, the ROM uses the first 16K of addresses,

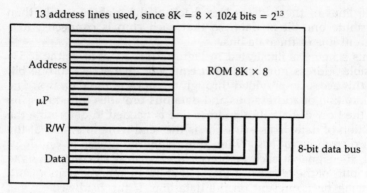

Figure 7.12 How an 8K ROM would be connected, using only 13 of the address lines

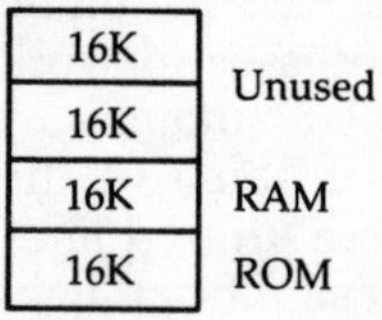

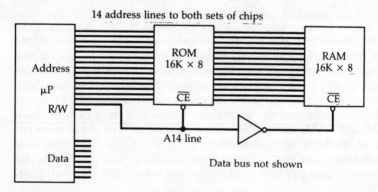

Figure 7.13 Memory mapping, using the lower 16K for ROM and the next 16K for RAM

14 address lines to both sets of chips

Figure 7.14 The connections for memory mapping of the type in Fig. 7.13. The A14 line is used to switch the chip-enable inputs of the memory chips, switching ROM and RAM alternately. This switching action will mean that the mapping is duplicated on the upper 16K blocks

and the RAM uses the next 16K. Now the important thing about this scheme is that 16K corresponds to 14 lines of an address bus, and the same 14 lines are used for both sets of memory. The principle is illustrated in Figure 7.14. The lower 14 address lines, A0 to A13, are connected to both sets of chips, represented here by single blocks. Line A14, however, is connected to 'chip enable' pins, which as the name suggests enable or disable the chips. The principle is simple. During the first 16K of addresses, line A14 is low, so that RAM is enabled (imagining the enable pin as being active when low) and ROM is disabled. For the next 16K of addresses on lines A0 to A13, A14 is high, so that RAM is disabled and ROM is enabled. This allows the same 14 address lines to carry out the addressing of both ROM and RAM. A simple scheme like this is possible only when both ROM and RAM occupy the same amount of memory and required the same number of address lines.

A very common scheme that was used for small computers is illustrated in Figure 7.15. The RAM consists of 8 chips of 64K × 1

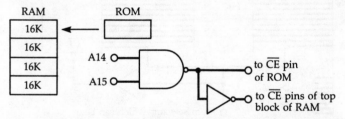

Figure 7.15 Memory-mapping ROM and RAM, in which the RAM chips provide for a full 64K of RAM, but the uppermost 16K is used by ROM

bit dynamic RAM, using the whole address range. The problem of how to deal with the ROM can then be dealt with in one of two ways. One is simply to map the ROM over some of the RAM. This means that a range of addresses will select ROM rather than RAM, and the RAM which exists in this range of addresses is never used. It looks wasteful but the falling prices of 64K RAM chips have, in fact, made a scheme of this type cheaper than a memory built up from 16K chips and with no redundant blocks. The ROM is selected by using OR gating, and Figure 7.15 illustrates the situation in which 16K at the top end of memory is used for ROM in this way.

The alternative, which is now becoming more common, is to use 'bank switching' schemes. Bank switching implies that the memory is laid out in banks which can be of up to 64K each, the size used in the very popular PC type of computer. A more common size, however, for smaller-scale digital circuits is 16K. A bank is switched either in or out, and when switched in it uses the range of memories to which it is mapped. The switching is carried out by using the enable pin on each chip. Suppose, for example, that the arrangement in Figure 7.16 is used. This illustrates a full 64K

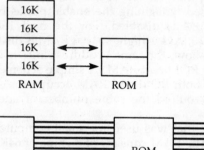

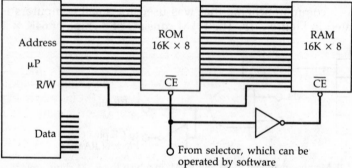

From selector, which can be operated by software

Figure 7.16 Bank switching, in which the ROM and RAM share some of the same address range, and are switched in and out according to requirements. This allows the use of both ROM and RAM in the same address range

of RAM, with 32K of ROM addressed by the lines A0 to A14. When the ROM is switched in, then, the lower 32K of memory consists of ROM, and the upper 32K of RAM. When the ROM is switched out, the whole 64K consists of RAM. Unlike the previous schemes for mapping memory, however, this type cannot rely entirely on hardware. Any writing operation must, of course, be to RAM since ROM cannot be written, but the problem is how to allocate reading. Some reading actions will be from the RAM, since the RAM contains program data. Other reading must be from the ROM, which contains the fixed routines, such as input/output, and also any programming language. The solution is to use software for switching. The ROM contains, in this example, two routines which switch banks. One switches in the RAM, the other switches in the ROM, and the actual switching is done by sending a 1 or a 0 to a 'port address', so causing a 1 or 0 to appear on a line that controls the enable pins on the memory chips. When the computer is switched on, a routine places into a section of the RAM memory a copy of these ROM addresses. This part of the RAM must be one that is not bank switched. When the machine is initially switched on, the RAM is switched in. Any call to a routine in the ROM must then make use of a coding which will first switch in the ROM. Precisely how this can be done depends on the instruction set for the microprocessor chip, and the ingenuity of the software writer.

The allocation of memory is considerably easier for the chips that can address greater amounts of memory. Using a 20 pin address system, for example, allows 1024K (1M) of memory to be addressed, with no switching tricks needed. This does not necessarily make these chips easier to work with. One of the problems for designers is the chip package itself. If the conventional 40-pin inline package is retained, it is not possible to cater for 20 address lines, and at the same time, for more than 8 data lines. One way out, taken by the earlier 16-bit chips, was to use an 8-bit data bus, and rely on the additional memory capabilities, plus a high clock speed, to perform at a reasonable speed. This approach has not resulted in speeds significantly greater than those of good 8-bit designs using bank switching.

An alternative, then, has been to multiplex pin use, a system that is used for dynamic RAM chips in the form of *row* and *column* pins. Each address can be obtained by placing one number on a set of 'row' pins and another on a set of 'column' pins. This results in considerable hardware complications, and reduces the processing speed to a smaller fraction of the clock rate. This can be compensated for by designing the chip so that it can use higher clock rates.

8 The microprocessor

A microprocessor is a programmable logic chip which can make use of memory. The microprocessor can address memory, meaning that it can select stored data and make use of it, or place such data into memory at an address chosen within the microprocessor. Within the microprocessor chip itself, logic actions such as the standard NOT, AND, OR and XOR actions can be carried out, as well as a range of other actions such as shift and rotate (the straight-ring counter action), and some simple arithmetic. The fact that any sequence of such actions can be carried out under the control of a program is the final item that completes the definition of a microprocessor.

In general, microprocessors are designed so as to fall into one of two classes. One type is intended for industrial control, and this also extends to the control of domestic equipment, such as central heating systems. A microprocessor of this type will often be almost completely self-contained, with its own memory built in, and very often this will include the programming instructions. Such microprocessors will very often need to work with a limited number of binary digits (bits) at a time, perhaps four. The number of possible programming instructions need only be small. The control microprocessor will also be offered typically as a 'semi-custom' device, with the programming instructions put in at the time of manufacture for one particular customer. By contrast, the alternative is the type of microprocessor whose main purpose is computing. The computer type contains little or no memory of its own, but is capable of addressing large amounts of external memory. It will deal with at least eight bits, and more usually 16 or 32 bits of data at a time. It has a much larger range of instructions, and will generally operate at high speeds.

The microprocessor story

The development of the microprocessor was a set of events which consisted partly of accidents, partly of strokes of genius, and partly of good marketing. The origin of the microprocessor was a military contract, placed in the later 1960s, for a programmable controller chip. The contract, like so many of its kind, was cancelled just at the time when production was starting, and the company was left with a production line which had been paid for, but which could make only devices that no-one wanted. The device was what we would now call a 4-bit microprocessor, the Intel 4004. For some time, this looked like the answer to a problem that no-one had, but some good marketing activity stimulated engineers to consider the possibilities of a single-chip device which could carry out the actions that until then had required a large assembly of boards. Machine control was one obvious outlet, and the startling new one was the microcomputer.

The 4004 then spawned the 8008, the first 8-bit microprocessor, and this brought about the possibility of really powerful low-cost small-size computers. When the 8008 was developed into the 8080, and Gary Kildall developed the CP/M operating system for small computers, the microcomputer industry as we know it now began the remarkable growth that slowed only in 1985. It's a classic US story of brilliant design, accidents and taking advantage of opportunities.

Construction

Registers and gates are the building blocks of microprocessors just as they are the building blocks of memory chips. The microprocessor is a more complicated device, but in essence it consists of registers which are connected through gates. This is the important feature that ultimately makes the microprocessor a programmable device. Imagine, to start with, that we have three one-bit registers (flip-flops) which are connected by gates as illustrated in Figure 8.1. The outputs of either register A or register B can be connected to register C through the gates. If gate 1 is enabled and gate 2 disabled, then the output of register A is connected to register C, and the bit will be transferred at the next clock pulse. If gate 2 is enabled and gate 1 disabled, then the transfer will be from register B to register C. In this example, the output from the registers has been used to provide the input for another register, but it could

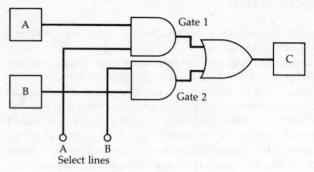

Figure 8.1 Using binary signals to select a path between registers, the fundamental action of the microprocessor

equally well have provided the input to another gate. The important point is that the signal path has been controlled by signals to two gates, and if we wanted to control a set of eight signals instead of one, then the same principles apply.

The next point is how the gate signals are to be applied. Getting back to the simple single bit control system, we needed two signals to the gates. For connecting registers A and C, we needed gate 1 enabled, gate 2 disabled. For connecting registers B and C we needed gate 1 disabled, gate 2 enabled. These two cases require signals of 10 (A to C) or 01 (B to C) at the gate inputs 1 and 2 respectively. We could disable both gates by using 00, but we'll leave that possibility for the moment. The next step is to imagine that the gate inputs are provided from a register, Figure 8.2. The

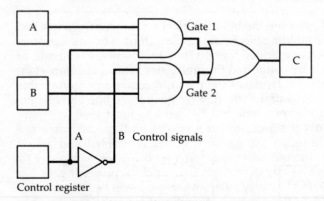

Figure 8.2 Using a register to store the binary signals, so that a bit placed in this register controls the signal paths

output of the register can be connected to the input of gate 1, and through an inverter to gate 2. In this way, if the output of the register is a 1, then gate 1 is enabled, gate 2 is disabled, and registers A and C are connected. Making the output of this control register equal to zero will reverse the gating, and connect registers B and C. This one simple step has, however, made our simplified circuit into a programmable device! The programming is carried out by storing a bit in the control register, because that bit will then determine the signal paths between the other registers. Programming now consists of placing suitable bits into a control register, so that the gating circuits can then make the correct connections between registers. Though this has been a simplified explanation, all of the principles are identical. For a microprocessor, then, there will be a control register which will be used to contain bits that open or close gates and so make or break connections between other registers.

Before we abandon this simple model of a programmable device, though, we can use it to demonstrate another point about programmable operation. The timing of the operations is very important for any programmable action. In the simple example, the bit that controls the gates must be in place, in the control register, before the transfer of bits between registers can take place. Because of the type of register construction that is used, this means that the action of transferring a bit from one register to another would require two clock pulses. On the first clock pulse, the control register would accept the programming bit. On the second clock pulse, the registers A or B would be connected to register C and the bit transferred. In the simple circuits of Figures 8.1 and 8.2, of course, there are always register connections between A and

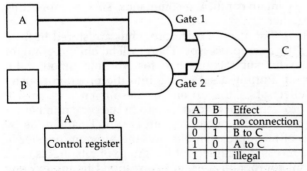

A	B	Effect
0	0	no connection
0	1	B to C
1	0	A to C
1	1	illegal

Figure 8.3 A two-bit control register in use for the same example

C or B and C whether there is a 1 or a 0 in the control register. It isn't difficult, however, to imagine the system extended so that the no-connection option was possible, using 0 signals into both gates. This means that the outputs from the control register have to use two bits instead of 1, and be capable of decoding the combinations 00, 01 and 10. The simplest method is to use a 2-bit control register as in Figure 8.3, using the bits directly. Now with nothing loaded into the control register, there is no input for register C. The other inputs 01 and 10 make connections — but we can't use 11 because that would connect both registers! We could imagine, however, that the 11 output could be decoded in some other way — such as enabling another set of connections between registers — if suitable gating existed. Once again, it all boils down to the use of the control register, but now we have the complication that for the system as we have it so far, two clock pulses are needed to complete the operation.

Program register and microprogram

Each microprocessor chip will contain a form of control register, which is called the program register. This will be of as many bits as the microprocessor is designed to handle at a time, usually 8 or 16. Whatever is put into this program register completely decides what the microprocessor will do on the next few clock cycles, and so access to this register is very severely limited. Most of the bytes that it deals with, in fact, come from a preset group that are permanently stored within the microprocessor, called the microprogram. By using this system, the makers of microprocessors avoid the need to have to check each input to the microprocessor, in case it should contain conflicting commands, such as connecting all registers together.

The principle is that a set of microprograms are stored in fixed memory inside the microprocessor. There will be one program for adding, another for subtracting, one for ANDing, another for ORing and so on. Putting a set of bits into the program register will have the effect of calling up one of these microprograms. If the bits in the program register correspond to the code number for a microprogram, then the microprogram is run. This is done by feeding groups of microprogram bits into the program register in turn until the process is complete. If the group of bits that is used to call up the microprogram does not correspond to any existing microprogram, then the command is ignored. In this way, the gating within the microprocessor is controlled in a more predictable way, one that has been determined by the manufacturers and is built into the chip. This set is called the *command set*.

The next part of the puzzle is how the program register can be loaded with a command in the first place. This is dealt with by part of the microprogramming. When the microprocessor is switched on, its first action will be to load in a byte or word, according to whether it is an 8-bit or 16-bit device. This first byte or word is gated directly into the program register, and then these gates are disabled. If this byte or word now calls up a microprogram, the program register is then supplied from the internal microprogram, and external signals from the pins of the chip are connected to other registers. Only following the last microprogram action are the gates which connect from the pins into the program register enabled again so that another command byte/word can be read. In this way, the microprocessor reads commands only when it is ready for them. Since each action is triggered by the arrival of a clock pulse, the timing is always exact, and each instruction will take a fixed (different) number of clock pulses to run its microprogram.

Take, for example, the process of adding two numbers. For the sake of simplicity, we will imagine that the numbers are already stored in two registers, and the result will be returned to one of the registers. The action of addition is started when the microprocessor reads an ADD instruction byte or word. This will be taken from the external memory, something that we shall look at in more detail shortly. The ADD instruction will be read directly into the program register, which is then shut off as far as external signals are concerned. By analysing the bits of the instruction, the correct microprogram is called up. The first part of the microprogram is then loaded into the program register, and its action is to connect one register to one set of the inputs to an adder. This action requires one clock pulse, and on the next clock pulse, the other register is connected to the other set of adder inputs. The next clock pulse provides the next microprogram instruction, which connects the (stored) output of the adder back to the input of one register. The next clock pulse brings in the microprogram action which enables the gates, so adding the bits and then storing the result back on the next clock pulse. The last microprogram action must then re-enable the gates which allow a command to enter the program register from outside the microprocessor.

As usual, this is over-simplified, particularly as regards the clock pulses, which are also gated to the correct places. The principle however, is sound—that the actions in the ADD routine are decided by the microprogram which has been called into action by a single instruction. In addition, we have established the very important point that this single instruction reaches the program register only when gates are enabled, and that for most of the time, the program register is not accessible to signals from outside the microprocessor. Another important principle is that all actions are carried out in sequence, one stage of action for each step in the microprogram. Finally, all of the actions are controlled by the clock pulses, and the speed of all processing depends on the speed of these clock signals. The construction of many types of microprocessor chips makes it impossible to observe the action with slow clock pulses. This is because signal voltages leak from one point to another within the microprocessor, and it's only at high clock speeds that the time for leakage becomes so short that the voltage levels are not significantly affected. As a rough rule of thumb, microprocessors should not be run at a clock speed much below 100 kHz. This does not apply to some CMOS types, such as the Intel HCMOS 80C86, which can be run at clock speeds down to zero! This allows the device to be clocked, if needed, by a push-button, so that the actions can be analysed in detail. The maximum clock speed is determined by the design of the microprocessor, particularly the stray capacitances. For modern microprocessors, maximum clock speeds in the range of 4 MHz to 24 MHz are common. Since the clock rate decides the rate of processing, microprocessors used in computers are usually run as fast as the chip can reliably cope with.

Clocking

From what we have studied so far, it's obvious that the clock pulse is the master timing pulse of any microprocessor system. The specification of the clock pulse in terms of frequency, rise and fall times and pulse shape is rather exacting. Some microprocessor chips include their own oscillator circuits, so that the only external components that need to be connected are a quartz crystal of the correct resonant frequency, and a few other discrete components. More often, the clock is an external circuit which can be a chip supplied by the makers of the microprocessor, or a circuit constructed from logic gates of the TTL LS class. Figure 8.4 shows a typical clock specification for a microprocessor working with a clock frequency in the 2–5 MHz range. The rise and fall times are

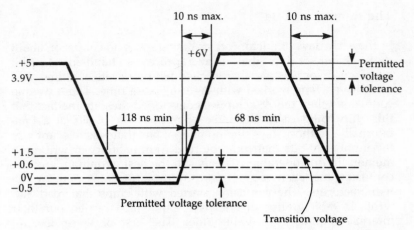

Figure 8.4 A typical clock-pulse specification for a modern microprocessor

particularly important, because long rise and fall times can cause considerable timing problems in circuits that use microprocessors. The specification of a minimum clock frequency, which can be as high as 8 MHz for a microprocessor that normally operates with a 12 MHz clock, reflects the high leakage inside the chip, due to very close packing of tracks.

The requirement for maintaining short rise and fall times for the clock pulse means that some care has to be taken with circuitry around the clock terminals of the microprocessor. This is not difficult if the clock circuits are built into the chip, or even if an external clock is used, because this can be located near the clock input pin of the microprocessor. Problems are more likely to be encountered when a co-processor is used, another microprocessor running along with the main microprocessor. This co-processor will need to be supplied with the same clock pulse, usually in phase, and with the same requirements of rise and fall times. Unless this co-processor can be located on the same board and very close to the main processor, the stray capacitance of PCB tracks, along with the load capacitance of the clock input pins of the co-processor, can cause degradation of the pulse shape. The problem is very much greater if the co-processor is located on another board. In this case, the use of Schmitt trigger stages both at the output from the main clock and the input to the co-processor clock will usually be needed to maintain fast rise and fall times.

The number of bits

In the early days of microprocessors there was no confusion about the number of bits that a microprocessor handled. A 4-bit microprocessor was one that worked with four bits at a time, and an 8-bit machine worked with eight bits at a time. There was no confusion when the Z80 chip was developed, despite the fact that this chip could carry out some operations on 16-bits at a time internally. In those days, the number of bits that was relevant was the number of bits that could be read from memory or written to memory in one operation. This is still the best definition, and the confusion has been caused more by users of chips than by the manufacturers. The confusion started with chips that read and wrote in 8-bit groups of one byte, but which carried out their internal operations in 16-bit units. The first of these 8/16 bit machines were the TMS 9900 family from Texas Instruments, and the most widely used chip of this type is the Intel 8088, as fitted to the original IBM PC. Another chip of this type is the Motorola 68008, which reads and writes in 8-bit units, but which has a 32-bit internal capability. I must make it clear that there is nothing makeshift or compromised about these types of chips. The main restriction of the 8-bit chip is that it has traditionally used 16 bits of memory addressing. This restricts the memory that can be addressed (without memory switching) to 64K. The restriction of the data in and out to eight bits is much less important. For applications such as word-processing, in which all data consists of eight bits or less, an 8-bit data group is ideal. The advantage of the 8/16 type of microprocessor chip is that it can often permit addressing much larger amounts of memory, typically 512K, but with the ability to use the same memory layouts, and, even more importantly, very similar software, as compared to the older types of 8-bit machines.

Hexadecimal numbers

Whatever number of bits constitutes the unit, the 8-bit *byte* or the 16-bit *word* or 32-bit *double-word*, the binary scale is very seldom used in writing by either hardware or software specialists because of the possibilities of confusion that can exist when numbers contain a large amount of 1's and 0's. In place of binary, the hexadecimal scale is used (octal, scale of eight was previously used) with a base of 16, and with the letters A to F used to indicate the numbers we write in denary as 10 to 15. Hexadecimal (hex) is particularly well suited to working with byte units, because a single byte of binary can be represented by two hex digits, and a word by four digits. These hex numbers are distinguished by starting the number with 0X or by ending it with H, so that 0X200A and 200AH are both valid ways of writing the number which is hex 200A, denary 8202. Appendix C contains a brief summary of hex notation.

Reading and writing

We have seen in Chapter 7 that memory for a microprocessor circuit can be arranged so that addresses and data can be sent over bus lines, allowing data to be exchanged among all the devices connected to the bus. Reading, as applied to a microprocessor, means that the data signals on the data bus are copied into a register within the microprocessor. As we have seen earlier, the first of a set of such data signals will always be copied into the instruction register. I have used the word 'copied' to emphasise that the process does not involve any kind of transfer, only a sharing action. The reading of memory by the microprocessor, for example, is rather like the reading of a tape by a tape-recorder. The signals are shared, but this does not involve the memory being cleared. When the microprocessor reads a memory location, then, the bits of that memory location are completely unaffected, and the only changes take place within the microprocessor, with a register in the microprocessor being set into the same bit arrangement. The action of writing is another copying action which means that the bits in a register of the microprocessor are made available on the data bus, and used to alter either memory or another external register. When writing is to memory, the memory content will be changed, but the content of the register of the microprocessor which provides the signal is not.

Both reading and writing are actions which cause change, either in a microprocessor register or in the memory, and change takes time. If we restrict ourselves at the moment to talking only about the use of the memory, there is another time delay involved. To read from or write to memory means that a set of memory cells must be selected. In a 64K × 1-bit memory, for example, one bit in each chip must be selected. This is done, as we have seen, by the signals on the address bus, but some time will inevitably elapse between the signals on the bus becoming steady, and the memory selection becoming complete. This time is a quoted parameter for each type of memory chip, and a typical figure for the memory fitted in small computers is of the order of 200 ns. To this we need to add the time between getting the address bits into a register in the microprocessor, and the voltages on the lines becoming steady. Typical times for this operation are 10 to 100 ns. If a modest 4 MHz clock rate is being used, then the clock voltage will be high for around 120 ns, and low for another 120 ns, so that you cannot expect a memory to be read or written to in the same clock cycle as started the addressing process. It would obviously be disastrous to attempt to read from memory or write to memory until the memory selection was complete, so that the timing of microprocessor operations is of vital importance. This timing is provided for in the design of the microprocessor, a topic that is beyond the scope of this book.

Bus actions

One very important feature of bus lines which has not been brought out so far is 'three-state' control. This, as noted earlier, does not imply a third logic state voltage, but the ability to 'float' a line so that any clash of bus use will not cause damage. The signals of the control bus, applied to the three-state control pins, can then determine the times at which external devices can make use of the buses, with the bus pins of the microprocessor floating. The designer of a microprocessor system then must ensure that any other devices which can place voltages on the buses are controlled by the appropriate timing signals so that they will be effective only when the bus is in its third-state of floating. All of the address pins and data pins of a microprocessor are of this three-state type, and several of the control bus line also. All microprocessors use similar address and data lines, but the signals on the control bus vary considerably from one microprocessor to another, and it isn't always obvious which of the control bus signals may be capable of three-state operation. If you are reading this book with the intention of designing or servicing microprocessor equipment, you should realise that it is essential to read the manufacturer's manuals closely in order to find, for any particular device, which lines are three-state, and which control lines are active at various times in the cycle.

Control bus

As you will have gathered by now, the principles of address bus and data bus are common to all microprocessors, and the only real complication in this respect is the use of multiplexing as on chips such as the Intel 8086. The control bus, however, is something that is very specific to a microprocessor type, and even microprocessors in the same family of devices can differ significantly from each other. In this section, then, we shall examine some typical control signals that are used by several popular microprocessor types. At this point, it's important to note the polarity of signals. In the early types of microprocessors, the convention was that a bus line was 'active low', meaning that the signal took effect when the voltage changed from logic 1 to logic 0. This was invariably indicated in the name of the signal by placing a bar over the abbreviated name. More recent designs of microprocessor use a mixture of control signals, some of which are active low, others active high. It's more usual now to find in application sheets the words 'active' and 'inactive' used of these signals, to avoid having to specify high or low for each one. Great care must therefore be taken to find out which state is the active one, and if you are using a microprocessor type for the first time, it's always a good idea to type out a reminder sheet for yourself.

Some control bus signals are inevitably the same on almost any microprocessor. One obvious example is the use of RD and WR signals to control the reading or writing of RAM. Older types of microprocessor, such as the Motorola 6800 and Mostek 6502, used a single R/W line, which was placed at logic 1 for read, logic 0 for write. Later types tended to use separate pins for RD and WR, so that a state of neither reading nor writing could be more easily arranged. The Z80 uses this system, with the two signals on adjacent pins, both active low, and both three-state. This scheme is the normal one, but the modern microprocessor chips tend to use these pins for more than one function.

One control signal type which is found on all microprocessors, almost regardless of design or manufacture, is the RESET. The purpose of the RESET signal of the control bus is, as the name suggests, to reset the microprocessor so that the next clock pulse will behave as if it were the first pulse after switch-on. This means that the microprocessor must have in its PC register (see later) the first address of a routine which will do whatever needs to be done at switch-on, or at any restart. The design of the microprocessor will determine what address must be used. On the Z80, for example, the RESET signal on pin 26 is active low. Its effect is to enable any interrupt (see later), and to clear the program counter (addressing) register, along with two other registers, the interrupt register and the refresh register. During the time that the reset line is low, the address and data buses are kept in their isolated state, and the other control bus signals are inactive. No memory refresh is being carried out in this state. Normal action will start from address 0000 when the RESET pin voltage rises to logic 1 again. On the Intel 8086, by contrast, the RESET signal on pin 21 must be high to be active, and must be held high for at least four clock cycles. Any action that was being carried out is ended immediately the RESET line is taken high, and the restart will take place when the pin voltage is allowed to drop to zero again. During the reset, address and data buses are in the isolated state, and the control bus signals assume settings with some pins high, some low, others taken momentarily high before taking up an isolated state. The microprocessor will remain dormant for as long as the reset voltage remains high, and the restoration of normal services will start when the voltage on the reset pins goes low again. This takes about 10 clock cycles, and after this time, the address in the PC register will be (in hex) FFFF0H. This means that the software designer must place in the memory addresses FFFF0H to FFFFFH a routine that will initialise the microprocessor after any reset action. When the microprocessor is first switched on, the RESET action must not occur until at least 50 μs after power has been applied.

The HALT or WAIT action is also one that is implemented on a number of different microprocessors in ways that do not, on the surface, look alike. The more modern microprocessors in particular, use a HALT action which allows another microprocessor to take over the buses, and this is normally an action that requires a confirming signal. The HALT is started by changing the voltage on one pin, but the buses are not available until the voltage on another pin has changed. On the Z80, the HALT signal is sent out from the microprocessor to indicate that the action has been halted. The actual halt is, in this case, achieved by using a software instruction, and the microprocessor will remain halted until triggered off again by an interrupt signal. While the HALT line is low, the microprocessor continues to address memory and carry out refresh actions so that dynamic memory retains its data. The microprocessor action can be halted also by taking the WAIT pin low. This inhibits the transfer of data in or out, and will do so for as long as the pin voltage is held low. Once again, normal addressing and memory refresh actions are continued.

The PC register and addressing

The microprocessor runs a program by outputting address numbers on the address bus, so as to select memory. At each memory address, data will be read, to obtain an instruction or the data to carry out an instruction; or written to store in memory. The sequence of reading memory is normally a simple incrementing order, so that a program which starts at address 0000H will step to 0001H, 0002H and so on, automatically as each part of the program is executed. The exception is in the case of a jump, caused by an interrupt or by a software instruction. A jump in this sense means that a new address will be placed into the program counter register, and the microprocessor wil then read a new instruction starting at this address. For the moment, however, the important point is that the normal action is one of incrementing the memory address each time a program action has been executed.

The program counter (PC) register is the main addressing register, connected by gates to the address pins of the microprocessor. The number in this register will be initialised at RESET, and incremented each time an instruction has been executed, or when an instruction calls for another byte. Imagine, for example, that the whole of the RAM memory from address 0000H is filled with a NOP instruction byte. NOP means 'no operation', and its action is simply to do nothing, just go on to the next instruction. If the PC is reset to contain the address 0000H, then the NOP byte at this address will be read, decoded, and acted on. The action is actually nil, and so the PC is incremented to address 0001H, the byte read, and the action repeated. If the entire memory is filled in this way, the microprocessor will simply cycle through all of the memory addresses until the address reaches 0000H again, and the whole addressing sequence will repeat. The time needed to cycle through memory in this way is very short. For a Z80 using a 4 MHz clock, for example, 64K of memory could be covered in a time of about 65 ms. For the Z80, the NOP instruction byte is 00H, so that the addressing of this particular chip can be checked by connecting all data lines to logic 0, and switching on. Other microprocessor types, however, do not necessarily use 00H as the NOP instruction.

Of course, in a real-life system, the memory is not full of NOP bytes. The timing and the PC actions depend very much on what instruction bytes are present, and even more so on the addressing method. Looking at addressing methods brings us into the realm of software, but is necessary for understanding how the PC and

175

buses can be used during an instruction that involves the use of memory. The principle is simple enough—that many of the instructions of the microprocessor require a byte (or more) to be obtained from the memory. Instructions like NOP, or the shift and rotate instruction do not normally require any load from memory. This is because these actions are carried out on a single byte or word, which can be stored in one of the registers of the microprocessor. For a lot of actions, though, one byte will be stored in a register, and another byte must be taken from memory. I shall use the example of a byte here, assuming the use of an 8-bit microprocessor, but the same principles apply to 16-bit microprocessors, using a word (2-bytes) rather than a byte.

Addressing methods

To illustrate addressing methods, we'll imagine that one byte, 31H is contained in the main arithmetic (accumulator) register of the microprocessor, and that we want to add to this a byte, 4BH, that will be taken from memory. The addressing method that is used will be determined mainly by software considerations, but the general aims are convenience and speed. The simplest, fastest and most convenient of the addressing methods is immediate addressing. When immediate addressing is used, the byte that has to be read from memory is stored immediately following the instruction byte. At the point in a program where we want to carry out the addition of the byte 4BH into the accumulator register we place the instruction byte. In the next memory address we place the 4BH byte. The action will be that when the PC increments to the address of this instruction byte, the instruction will be read into the instruction register, and decoded. As a result of decoding, a few clock cycles later, the data byte will be fetched from memory simply by incrementing the PC, placing this address on the bus, and carrying out a read action. The bytes 31H and 4BH are then added, and the result 7CH is placed back in the accumulator. Even this simplest addressing method has involved several steps of microprogram and anything from four to 16 clock pulses, depending on the microprocessor type. The attractiveness of this method is that the natural incrementing action of the PC is being used to obtain the data. The problem is that the method is not always the most practical. In a system which contained both ROM and RAM, you would normally want to hold a program in the ROM, and data in the RAM, but the use of immediate addressing requires the program and data to be mixed in together. This is just one reason why other methods may have to be used.

The main addressing method is called variously direct, extended, or absolute addressing. Suppose that the address of the byte 4BH is 7F23H. This address consists of two bytes, and can be stored in two single-byte memory locations. If we store, in sequence, an ADD instruction, then the two bytes of this address, we can make the microprocessor locate the 4BH byte from its memory address. This time, the ADD instruction byte will be different, because the action that is needed is different. The instruction byte is followed in the program memory by the two parts of the address, usually in low-high order. In other words, the address of 7F23H is stored as 23H, then 7FH. The sequence of actions for the addition is then as follows. First, the instruction byte is read into the instruction register for decoding. At the end of the decoding action, the PC is incremented so as to locate the low-byte of the address. When the address bus has settled, this byte is read and stored in a special address register. The PC is then incremented again, and with this new address on the bus, the high-byte of the address 7F23 is read, and is placed into the address register. The buses are then isolated, and the contents of the address register and the PC are exchanged. This puts the address 7F23H into the PC, and this address is now put on to the address bus. A read action will fetch the byte 4BH at this address, and from now on the addition action can take place as before. This has involved considerable use of the buses, plus an additional register, and an interchange. Finally, before the next instruction can be fetched, the PC and address registers are exchanged again, so that the address in the PC is once again the address of the high-byte 7FH. The PC is then incremented to prepare for fetching the next instruction byte. Like the program register, the register in which an address is assembled is not available to the software programmer, only to the microprogram.

Extended addressing of this type requires much more bus action, and inevitably takes much longer to execute than the simpler immediate addressing. Most microprocessor designs feature ingenious alternative addressing methods which allow faster addressing for special cases. An action that is very often needed in all kinds of applications is fetching a set of bytes in sequence. A set of bytes stored in order in the memory could be fetched by extended addressing, but it's much more convenient if the address of the first of the bytes can be stored in a register, and the register contents (the address) incremented each time a byte is fetched. In this way, the buses are used much less, once to fetch the instruction byte, and once to fetch the byte from memory, with no need to use two fetch operations to assemble an address each time. Addressing of this type is featured on most modern microprocessors, and was also a feature of the Z80 and its immediate ancestor, the 8080.

Interrupts

An interrupt is, as the name suggests, a signal that interrupts the normal action of the microprocessor and forces it to do something else. That 'something else' almost always means a routine which starts at a different address, and which will carry out an action that deals with the needs of the interrupt signal. Such a routine is called an 'interrupt service routine'. This simple description leaves a lot unanswered. For example, suppose that the microprocessor is halfway through an instruction when an interrupt occurs? What then happens to that instruction? How can the microprocessor resume its normal program actions after an interrupt, when the interrupt service routine has forced the microprocessor to jump to a new address? What happens if another interrupt comes along when the microprocessor is dealing with an interrupt already? We'll deal with these points later, and for the moment concentrate on why an interrupt system is used before we examine the details of how it is implemented.

Suppose, for example, that the microprocessor is working in a loop, repeating a set of instructions over and over again, as is required for simply displaying something on the screen. How would you make certain that presssing a key on the keyboard would cause the microprocessor to find the correct code for that key, and place the result on the screen? One way involves purely software. The loop that the microprocessor is performing must contain a test of the keys which will run a suitable routine if a key happens to be pressed. This is a system called 'polling', and the objection to it is that this test will run each time the loop runs, perhaps several thousand times per second, even if the keys are pressed only once per minute or so. The result is to make the loop run much less quickly than it would if it contained no key-testing portions. The alternative to this software method is a hardware *interrupt*. Pressing any of the keys on the keyboard generates an electrical signal which is applied to one of the interrupt pins of the microprocessor. When this signal is received, the microprocessor executes an interrupt routine. In doing so, it will complete the instruction that it is processing, and then jump to an address to get directions for a service routine, in this example, the routine that reads the keyboard. The fact that the current instruction is always completed answers one of the points about interrupts. This interrupt system allows the machine to operate at high speed in its normal processing, without the need to test for a key being pressed until the event happens. A compromise method that is used in several computers is to keep the key test routine separate, and to generate an interrupt 50 times per second (using the field synchronising pulses for the monitor display) to test the keys. The important point in all this is that an interrupt is a signal to a pin, and its effect must be to make a piece of program run. The use of interrupts, then, concerns both hardware and software designers.

Before we go any further, we must attend to the other two questions about interrupts, and answer another one which arises. The first question, about completing an instruction, has already been answered. The second point, about returning to the correct address, is dealt with automatically. All microprocessors allow a part of the memory to be designated as a 'stack'. This means simply that some addresses are used by the microprocessors for storing register contents, making use of the memory in a very simple last-in-first-out way, a hangover from the early types of serial memory. Precisely which addresses are used in this way is generally a choice for the software designer. Early types of microprocessors forced designers to set aside fixed addresses, such as 0100H to 0200H, but the stack position is always a matter of choice nowadays, at least for computer microprocessors. When an interrupt is received, the first part of the action is for the microprocessor to complete the action on which it is engaged. The next item is to store the PC address in the stack memory. This action is forced by the microprogram so as far as the user is concerned, it is completely automatic. Only the address is stored in this way, however. If the interrupt service routine will change the contents of any other registers of the microprocessor, it will be necessary to save the contents of these registers on the stack also. This is something that has to be attended to by the programmer who writes the interrupt service routine, saving the register contents at the start of the interrupt service routine, and replacing them afterwards. Finally, the problem of multiple interrupts is dealt with by disabling the interrupt mechanism while an interrupt is being serviced. This is not necessarily automatic, and will often form one of the first items in the interrupt service routine.

As it happens, most microprocessors can make use of more than one type of interrupt signal. The two main types are maskable and non-maskable. A maskable interrupt is one that can be enabled or disabled by software instructions. This allows the software designer to disable interrupts at times when an interrupt would cause corruption of data. For example, when data is being loaded from a disk or stored onto a disk, the transfer of data is a strictly-timed operation. If pressing a key could interrupt this, the memory of the machine could contain a fraction of a program and the disk controller could be left midway through a sequence of actions. A software designer would therefore want to disable any interrupts while a disk load (or save) was being executed or at any time when another interrupt was being serviced. There may, however, be events (such as pressing a special BREAK key) which must cause an interrupt, and this need is catered for by a non-maskable interrupt. The normal method of dealing with this double system is to have two separate interrupt pins on the body of the microprocessor.

Recent developments

This has been a very brief summary of a large amount of information which could fill a book by itself, but it would hardly be possible to write a book on digital devices without mentioning the microprocessor. The main advantage in using a microprocessor is that the same circuit of microprocessor and memory can carry out any sequence of digital actions. The hardware solution to a digital problem is to design a specific circuit, the microprocessor solution is to take a standard circuit, perhaps a single chip, and to carry out the actions by a set of software instructions, in sequence. The drawback of this is contained in the key words *in sequence*, because this implies that more time is needed to carry to a set of digital actions using a microprocessor than using a custom-designed circuit.

Recently, three diverging design trends have appeared in the design of microprocessor chips for computing. One group of microprocessors, predominant until recently, has evolved more and more complex instruction sets, making it possible to program the chips in very elaborate ways and with few instruction steps. This had led to chips with instruction sets so large that few designers ever use more than a fraction of the commands, some of which take an inordinate number of clock cycles to complete.

One alternative now is the RISC microprocessor, using a Reduced Instrument Set Chip. The basis of the RISC design is that most programs for microprocessors make intensive use of only a few instructions, so that the microprogram of a RISC chip contains only a few actions, each of which is arranged to be carried out at the maximum possible speed. One of the devices commonly used on such chips is to 'pipeline' instructions, so that a command byte or word is being read at the same time as a previous command is being executed. This is done by using a multi-phase clock, with reading on one phase and execution on another.

The RISC idea is not quite so new as it appears, because even in the early days of microprocessor design, chips like the 6502 were making use of small instruction sets and pipelining to achieve high speeds, and the idea faltered mainly because of the lack of development of chips of this type to 16-bit construction, along with the success of the more complex type of chips in computers such as the IBM PC. It is interesting that the main drive to RISC use in the UK has come from firms who formerly used the 6502 chips and who are therefore familiar with the ideas of programming with a limited instruction set.

The other trend is to very much more complex computing of a very different type. This makes use of the Transputer, a complete computer built on a single chip. The main application is to parallel processing, allowing actions to be carried out simultaneously by using several Transputers, rather than the conventional sequential method. The use of Transputers in this way demands a special programming language, OCCAM, and opens up the possibility, now being realised, of making comparatively low-cost desktop machines which have the computing speed and power of main-frame machines. Even more interesting is the use of Transputer add-on boards for conventional small computers (such as the Atari ST) in order to take over the running of routines that would occupy too much of the time of the main processor, such as graphical displays.

Appendix A
BS logic symbols

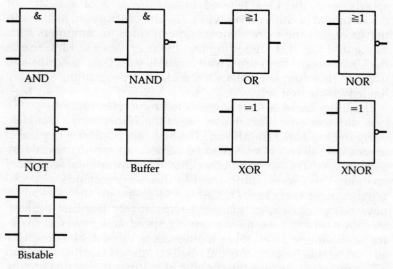

Figure A.1 BS gate and flip-flop symbols (BS 3939/IEC 117–51)

Appendix B
Serial communications

The idea of sending signals over wires is not exactly new; it was the basis of the electric telegraph, and we were sending data in this form by cable between the UK and France by 1850. The principle of the telegraph is to have a code of electrical signals for each letter, digit and punctuation mark of the language, and the Morse Code became the standard for this purpose very early on. The problem about digital signals is the number of them that we need to transmit for each character of data and the speed with which a digital device such as a computer deals with such signals. The main problem arises from having to send our signals one bit at a time, called serial transfer.

The serial transfer of data has the advantage of making use of only one line (plus a ground return) for data, with the data being transmitted one bit at a time at a strictly clock-controlled rate. When data is sent one bit at a time, the grouping of the data has to be standardised, and this is usually into bytes of eight bits each. In addition, some method has to be used to allow the receiving circuits to distinguish one group of eight bits from its neighbours. For a serial transmission there is just one line for the bits of data, and the eight data bits must be sent in turn and assembled into a byte by storing them in a register at the receiving end. The problem is that since one bit looks like any other, how does the receiving machine recognise the first bit of a byte? The way round the problem is to precede each transmitted byte of eight bits by a start bit (a zero) and end it by either one or two stop bits (each a 1) — notice that there is no standardisation of the number of stop bits, though one stop bit is slowly becoming the more common practice.

Ten (or eleven) bits must therefore be transmitted for each byte of data, and both transmitter and receiver must use the same number of stop bits. The transmitting circuits will send out their bytes of data, and at the receiving computer, the arrival of a start bit will start the machine counting in the bits of data, storing them into its memory until it has a set of eight, and then checking that it gets the correct number of stop bits after the last data bit. If the pattern of a zero, then eight bits (0 or 1), then a 1, is not found (assuming eight data bits and one stop bit), then the receiving circuits can be programmed to register a mistake in the data, and start counting again, looking back at the stored data and starting with the next 0 bit that could be a start bit. The recounting is fast, and can be carried out in the time between the arrival of one bit and the next, so that it would be unusual to miss more than one character in this way.

At this level, it would be more usual to use software to control the system so that these actions will be carried out automatically if, and only if, the software has been correctly programmed at each end of the link to work with the correct settings. The use of the same number of stop bits and data bits by both computers is not in itself enough to ensure correct transfer, though. In addition to using the same number of data bits and stop bits, both transmitter and receiver must work with the same number of bits per second.

All serially transmitted data (as distinct from programs) will almost certainly use ASCII code and if you are transmitting ASCII text only (not program data) this will require only seven of the eight data bits that can be sent. If only 7-bit ASCII is needed, then the eighth bit can be used as a parity bit, a check on the integrity of the data. The parity system can be of two types, even or odd. In the even parity system, the number of ON signals (logic 1's) in the remainder of the byte is counted, and the parity bit is made either 1 or 0 so that the total number of 1's is then even. In the odd parity system, the parity bit will be adjusted so as to make the number of 1's an odd number. At the receiver, the parity can be checked and an error reported if the parity is found to be incorrect. This simple scheme will detect a single-bit error in a byte, but cannot detect multiple errors nor can it correct errors. Since it is applicable only when 7-bit data is being transmitted, it is used mainly for text transmissions, and nowadays is often omitted altogether. Small errors in text can easily be corrected visually, and for program transfer much better methods of detecting and correcting errors need to be used.

Good software can make use of these other methods of adding data so as to provide for better checking and can even provide for correction of errors to some extent. The checking methods can range from the simple checksum, through cyclic redundancy checking (CRC), to the very complicated Reed-Solomon system (also used in compact discs), but they all have one factor in common, redundancy. All checking involves sending more bits or bytes than the bytes of the data, with the extra bits or bytes carrying checking and error-correcting signals. Some of these can work on individual bytes, even on individual bits; others are intended to work on complete blocks of 128 bytes or more. The checksum, for example, works by adding the number values of all of the ASCII codes in a set number of bytes, often 128. This sum is transmitted as a separate byte, and at the receiver the codes are again summed and the total compared with the transmitted checksum. Only if the two match will the set of bytes be accepted, and if they don't the transmitter is requested to send the block of data again.

Because these checking methods all involve the transmission of extra bytes, they slow down the rate of communication of useful data. For text transmissions, the use of elaborate checking is often unnecessary because an occasional mistyped character in text is often not important compared to the need for a high speed of transmission. For sending other data, however, one false byte is usually enough to ensure that the data is useless, so that much better checking methods must be used even if this means taking longer to transmit the data. You often have to select, by way of your communications software, different methods for transmitting different types of data.

The individual items of number of data bits, number of stop bits and use of even, odd or no parity make up what we call the modes serial *protocols*. You can't get very far in communications without knowing something about protocols, because unless both the transmitter and the receiver are using identical protocols there will be no communication, and only gibberish will be received. There is no single protocol that is used by everyone, so you need to be able to set your communications software to the protocol that is being used by the machine to which you want to be linked. The use of computers along with modern software makes this considerably easier than it used to be, but you still need to know what protocols are being used by the computer with which you are trying to communicate.

Appendix C
The hexadecimal scale

A machine code program for a microprocessor consists of a set of number codes. Since each number code is a way of representing the 1's and 0's in a byte, it will consist of numbers between 0 and 255 (for a single byte) or between 0 and 65535 (word size) when we write it in our normal scale of ten (denary scale). The program is useless until it is fed into the memory, because the microprocessor is a fast device, and the only way of feeding it with bytes as fast as it can use them is by storing the bytes in the memory, and letting the microprocessor help itself to them in order. You can't possibly type numbers fast enough to satisfy the microprocessor, and even methods like tape or disk are just not fast enough.

Getting bytes into the memory, then is an essential part of making a machine code program work. At one time, simple and very short programs would be put into a memory by the most primitive possible method, using eight switches. Each switch could be set to give a 1 or 0 electrical output, and a button could be pressed to cause the memory to store the number that the switches represented, and then select the next memory address. Programming like this is just too tedious, though, and working with binary numbers of 1's and 0's soon makes you cross-eyed. Now that we have computers, it makes sense to use the computer itself to put numbers into memory, either from disks or by using programming languages, and an equally obvious step is to use a more convenient numbers scale.

Just what is a more convenient number scale is a matter that depends on how you enter the numbers and how much machine code programming you do, if any. Even if you confine yourself to hardware, however, the use of the hexadecimal scale is forced upon you, not least by items such as interrupt address vectors. All single-byte numbers can be represented by just two hex digits, and words by four digits, and virtually all of the information that you can get about a microprocessor will have address numbers and data numbers in hex.

Hexadecimal means scale of 16, and the reason that it is used so extensively is that it is naturally suited to representing binary bytes. Four bits, half of a byte, will represent numbers which lie in the range 0 to 15 in our ordinary number scale. This is the range of one hex digit (Figure C.1). The number codes that are used as instructions have been designed in hex code, so that we can see much better how commands are related. For example, we may find that a set of related commands all start with the same digit when they are written in hex. In denary, this relationship would not appear. In addition, it's much easier to write down the binary number which the computer actually uses when you see the hex version. Converting between binary and hex is much simpler than converting between binary and denary.

The hexadecimal scale consists of 16 digits, starting as usual with 0 and going up in the usual way to 9. The next figure is not 10, however, because this would mean one sixteen and no units, and since we aren't provided with symbols for digits beyond 9, we use the letters A to F. The number that we write as 10 (ten) in denary is written as 0A in hex, eleven as 0B, twelve as 0C and so on up to fifteen, which is 0F. The zero doesn't have to be written, but programmers get into the habit of writing a data byte with two digits and an address or word with four even if fewer digits are needed. The number that follows 0F is 10, sixteen in denary, and the scale then repeats to 1F, thirty-one, which is followed by 20. The maximum size of single byte, 255 in denary, is FF in hex. When we write hex numbers, it's usual to mark them in some way so that you don't confuse them with denary numbers. There's not much chance of confusing a number like 3E with a denary number, but a number like 26 might be hex or denary. The convention that is followed by many programmers is to use a capital H to mark a hex number, with the H-sign placed after the number and often a 0 starting the number. For example, the number 047H means hex 47, but plain 47 would mean denary forty-seven. Another method is to use the hashmark before the number, so that #47 would mean the same as 47H. When you write hex numbers for any reason, it's advisable to follow one of these conventions.

Now the great value of hex code is how closely it corresponds to binary code. If you look at the hex-binary table of Figure 6.1, you can see that #9 is 1001 in binary and #F is 1111. The hex number #9F is therefore just 10011111 in binary—you simply write

The hexadecimal scale

Hex	Binary	Hex	Binary
0	0000	8	1000
1	0001	9	1001
2	0010	A	1010
3	0011	B	1011
4	0100	C	1100
5	0101	D	1101
6	0110	E	1110
7	0111	F	1111

Figure C1 Hex-binary equivalents table

Example: 02CH........................2H is 0010 binary
                                          CH is 1100 binary
so that 02CH is 00101100 binary, a single byte number.
Example: 04A7FH ....4H is 0100 binary
                                          AH is 1010 binary
                                          7H is 0111 binary
                                          FH is 1111 binary
so that 04A7FH is 01001010011111111 binary (a word)
                                 Conversion: Binary to Hex.
Example: 01101011 ....0110 is 6H
                                          1011 is BH
so that the byte 01101011 is 06BH
Example: 1011010010010 (not a complete number of bytes)
Group this into fours, starting with the lsb:
                                          0010 is 2H
                                          1001 is 9H
                                          0110 is 6H
                                          1 is 1H
so that the number is 01692H in hex.

Figure C2 Hex-binary conversion process

down the binary digits that correspond to the hex digits. Taking another example, the hex byte #B8 is 10111000, because #B is 1011 and #8 is 1000. The conversion in the opposite direction is just as easy—you group the binary digits in fours, starting at the least significant (right-hand) side of the number, and then convert each group into its corresponding hex digit. Figure C.2 shows examples of the conversion in each direction so that you can see how easy it is.

Index

Index